FOUR-PLACE TABLES
OF TRANSCENDENTAL FUNCTIONS

FOUR-PLACE TABLES

of

TRANSCENDENTAL FUNCTIONS

by

W. FLÜGGE

Dr.-Ing., Professor of Engineering Mechanics
at Stanford University

PERGAMON PRESS LTD. LONDON
1954

4.14.54

Published in Great Britain by Pergamon Press Ltd.
242 Marylebone Road, London, N.W.1.

Published in U.S.A. by McGraw-Hill Book Co., Inc.,
330 West 42nd Street, New York 36, N.Y.

Printed by J. W. Arrowsmith Ltd., Bristol, England

PREFACE

THERE was a time when sines and cosines were reserved for the use of learned men; today they are in the hands of a wide public—all those who use mathematics for some practical purpose—and even high-school boys have to face them. During our lifetime the exponential function and the hyperbolic sines and cosines have emerged from mathematical textbooks and have found their way into the world of engineers. And now some more of these transcendental functions—created in the past by speculative minds—are on their way into practical usefulness.

After a slow start in the nineteenth century the last two decades have seen admirable work in the computing and tabulating of mathematical functions, most of it done in the United States and in England. Many big volumes full of multidigit figures have been published, and they have become a treasure box of great value for those who need transcendental functions. But in spite of the rapid development of modern computing devices most computations are still done on the slide-rule, and for such kind of work the big original tables are somewhat unwieldy. The author felt that something was still missing for those who are old-fashioned enough to do their daily chores with the slide-rule, but modern enough to use mathematics beyond sines and cosines whenever that will help solve a problem.

For these men this little book has been compiled. It contains values, of slightly more than slide-rule accuracy, of those functions which are most likely to occur in a great many problems of physics and engineering. It also contains a collection of those formulas which are needed to handle the functions. They will suffice in many cases and may safely be used also by those who do not know all the mathematical theory that stands behind them.

Necessarily, the range of the tables had to be limited, and it will always be a controversial question where to stop. Some people may feel they could have done with less, but most users will some day need values for higher arguments. A compromise had to be made, and it was made so that beyond the end of the tables there are always *simple* means available to compute the missing values.

It is a matter of course that this book will not have " readers ". Nobody, except the proof-readers, will ever read it from cover to cover. But more than that: This book does not even want to be a book. It does not want to stand on your bookshelf, perhaps behind a glass door, well-kept, and dusted once a year. It wants to be a tool and to lie in the drawer where you keep your slide-rule, always at hand when its services may be required.

Although the preparation of these tables involved a good deal of computing, it would not have been possible to bring all this material together without ample use of existing table-literature. The author wishes in particular to express his thanks to the holders of copyright material who generously permitted its use for this work:

The BRITISH ASSOCIATION FOR THE ADVANCEMENT OF SCIENCE and the ROYAL SOCIETY in London for permission to extract the values of the Bessel functions Y_0, Y_1 ($0 \leqq x \leqq 10$) and of the modified Bessel functions K_0, K_1 ($0 \leqq x \leqq 5$) from the sixth volume of the Mathematical Tables of this Association.

Professor G. CASSINIS in Milan, Italy, for permission to extract values of the gamma-function from his table, mentioned on p. 118.

The author also owes a debt of gratitude to the various agencies of the United States Government who carried on the Mathematical Tables Project, producing tables of inestimable value.

Finally, the author has the pleasure of expressing his thanks to two of his colleagues, Professors J. N. GOODIER and K. KLOTTER, and to his wife, Dr. I. FLÜGGE-LOTZ, who had a critical look at the manuscript and helped to improve it by their constructive criticism.

Stanford University, California

February 1953   W. F.

CONTENTS

Instructions for the Use of the Tables

1. *Notations*

For many of the tabulated functions different notations are in current use. The ones adopted here are as close as possible to the most common usage.

For the hyperbolic functions the English symbols have been capitalized, since this has proved to be very helpful in avoiding mistakes in formulas. This change is suggested for general adoption.

For the Bessel functions and all functions connected with them the notation of WATSON'S Treatise has been adopted.

In the case of FRESNEL'S integrals there are two pairs of functions which are commonly designated by the same symbols C and S. Here those functions have been tabulated which have a constant distance between consecutive maxima and therefore are best suited for tabulation. It is suggested that the alternate meaning of the symbols C and S be entirely discarded.

2. *Arrangement of Tables*

Except for the elliptic integrals, all tables are arranged in the same manner as the common logarithmic tables. The first column contains all but the last digit of the argument x, and an additional digit of x is given by the headings of the other ten columns.

When reading the value of a function, the following rules apply:

A cipher before the decimal point has usually been omitted.

Examples: $\sin 45.0° = 0.7071$ appears on p. 15 as .7071; $\sin 3.40 = -0.2555$ appears on p. 19 as $-.2555$.

The columns 1 to 9 do not contain complete figures, and the first digits must be picked from the column 0. Usually they will be found on the same line or on a preceding line.

Examples: Tanh $0.72 = 0.6169$, Tanh $1.30 = 0.8617$, Tanh $1.31 = 0.8643$, Tanh $3.05 = 0.9955$ (p. 27), $\sin 3.43 = -0.2844$ (p. 19), $J_0 (8.92) = -0.07035$ (p. 48).

Where this rule does not hold, an asterisk has been provided as a sign that special attention is necessary. Usually the asterisk indicates that the first digit (or digits) will be found on the next following line [$\sin 0.52 = 0.4969$, but $\sin 0.53 = 0.5055$ (p. 19), $J_1 (2.83) = 0.3997$ (p. 47)], but occasionally it may mean something else [$\cos 3.14 = -1.0000$ (p. 18)].

Where a power of 10 has been factored out, it stands only on that line where it is first needed and is repeated only if the sign of the function changes.

Examples: Cosh $8.72 = 10^3 \times 3.062 = 3062$ (p. 26), bei $9.00 = -10 \times 2.471$
$= -24.71$ (p. 71), Ei $(-2.11) = -10^{-1} \times 0.4204 = -0.04204$ (p. 126).

Where a new power of 10 appears. the preceding line must be read throughout with the preceding power of 10, including the figures with an asterisk.

Examples: exp $9.21 = 10^3 \times 9.997$, exp $9.22 = 10^3 \times 10.097$,
exp $9.23 = 10^3 \times 10.20$ (p. 34), exp $(-9.21) = 10^{-3} \times 0.10003$,
exp $(-9.22) = 10^{-3} \times 0.09904$ (p. 35).

It will be noticed that at the transition one value is given with 5 digits in order to assure a 4-digit interpolation everywhere.

3. *Accuracy of Tables*

Most of the tables in this book may be expected to be as accurate as the limited number of digits permits; i.e. the error is not in excess of 0.5 units of the last digit carried. Many of the tables have been obtained by subtabulation from 6-digit source material. In these tables rounding errors in the sixth digit may occasionally influence the result so far that an error of 0.54 units of the last digit may occur. The tables of the Fresnel integrals are probably somewhat less accurate, since only LOMMEL'S table was available, which has a rather large interval and is not free from mistakes.

4. *Bibliography*

In the bibliography of the different sections only those tables have been mentioned which either give more digits or cover a wider range of arguments, and which were considered readily available in bookstores and libraries. For more detailed information the following books may be consulted:

A. FLETCHER, J. C. P. MILLER, L. ROSENHEAD: *An Index of Mathematical Tables*. New York and London, 1946;

Mathematical Tables and Other Aids to Computation. Published by the National Research Council since 1943.

Formulas

1. Power Series

$$\cos x = 1 - \frac{x^2}{2!} + \frac{x^4}{4!} - + \ldots \qquad \text{for any } x$$

$$\sin x = \frac{x}{1!} - \frac{x^3}{3!} + \frac{x^5}{5!} - + \ldots \qquad \text{for any } x$$

$$\tan x = x + \frac{x^3}{3} + \frac{2\,x^5}{15} + \frac{17\,x^7}{315} + \frac{62\,x^9}{2835} + \ldots \qquad \text{for } |x| < \frac{\pi}{2}$$

$$\cot x = x^{-1} - \frac{x}{3} - \frac{x^3}{45} - \frac{2\,x^5}{945} - \frac{x^7}{4725} - \ldots \qquad \text{for } |x| < \pi$$

2. Relations connecting the four functions

$$\cos x \qquad = \sqrt{1 - \sin^2 x} = \frac{1}{\sqrt{1 + \tan^2 x}} = \frac{\cot x}{\sqrt{1 + \cot^2 x}}$$

$$\sqrt{1 - \cos^2 x} = \quad \sin x \quad = \frac{\tan x}{\sqrt{1 + \tan^2 x}} = \frac{1}{\sqrt{1 + \cot^2 x}}$$

$$\frac{\sqrt{1 - \cos^2 x}}{\cos x} = \frac{\sin x}{\sqrt{1 - \sin^2 x}} = \quad \tan x \quad = \frac{1}{\cot x}$$

$$\frac{\cos x}{\sqrt{1 - \cos^2 x}} = \frac{\sqrt{1 - \sin^2 x}}{\sin x} = \frac{1}{\tan x} = \quad \cot x$$

3. Relation to the exponential function

$$\cos x = \tfrac{1}{2}\left(e^{ix} + e^{-ix}\right) \qquad\qquad \sin x = \frac{1}{2i}\left(e^{ix} - e^{-ix}\right)$$

$$e^{ix} \equiv \operatorname{cis} x = \cos x + i \sin x \qquad e^{-ix} = \cos x - i \sin x$$

4. Imaginary argument

$$\cos ix = \operatorname{Cosh} x \qquad \sin ix = i \operatorname{Sinh} x$$

$$\tan ix = i \operatorname{Tanh} x \qquad \cot ix = - i \operatorname{Coth} x$$

5. Addition theorems

$$\cos (x \pm y) = \cos x \cos y \mp \sin x \sin y$$

$$\sin (x \pm y) = \sin x \cos y \pm \cos x \sin y$$

$$\tan (x \pm y) = \frac{\tan x \pm \tan y}{1 \mp \tan x \tan y}$$

$$\cot (x \pm y) = \frac{\cot x \cot y \mp 1}{\cot y \pm \cot x}$$

Formulas

1. *Power series*

$$\text{Cosh } x = 1 + \frac{x^2}{2!} + \frac{x^4}{4!} + \ldots \qquad \text{for any } x$$

$$\text{Sinh } x = \frac{x}{1!} + \frac{x^3}{3!} + \frac{x^5}{5!} + \ldots \qquad \text{for any } x$$

$$\text{Tanh} x = x - \frac{x^3}{3} + \frac{2 x^5}{15} - \frac{17 x^7}{315} + \frac{62 x^9}{2835} - + \ldots \quad \text{for } |x| < \frac{\pi}{2}$$

$$\text{Coth } x = x^{-1} + \frac{x}{3} - \frac{x^3}{45} + \frac{2 x^5}{945} - \frac{x^7}{4725} + - \ldots \quad \text{for } |x| < \pi$$

2. *Relations connecting the four functions*

$$\text{Cosh } x = \sqrt{1 + \text{Sinh}^2 x} = \frac{1}{\sqrt{1 - \text{Tanh}^2 x}} = \frac{\text{Coth } x}{\sqrt{\text{Coth}^2 x - 1}}$$

$$\sqrt{\text{Cosh}^2 x - 1} = \text{Sinh } x = \frac{\text{Tanh } x}{\sqrt{1 - \text{Tanh}^2 x}} = \frac{1}{\sqrt{\text{Coth}^2 x - 1}}$$

$$\frac{\sqrt{\text{Cosh}^2 x - 1}}{\text{Cosh } x} = \frac{\text{Sinh } x}{\sqrt{1 + \text{Sinh}^2 x}} = \text{Tanh } x = \frac{1}{\text{Coth } x}$$

$$\frac{\text{Cosh } x}{\sqrt{\text{Cosh}^2 x - 1}} = \frac{\sqrt{1 + \text{Sinh}^2 x}}{\text{Sinh } x} = \frac{1}{\text{Tanh } x} = \text{Coth } x$$

3. *Relation to the exponential function*

$$\text{Cosh } x = \tfrac{1}{2}(e^x + e^{-x}) \qquad \text{Sinh } x = \tfrac{1}{2}(e^x - e^{-x})$$

$$e^x \equiv \exp x = \text{Cosh } x + \text{Sinh } x \qquad e^{-x} = \text{Cosh } x - \text{Sinh } x$$

4. *Imaginary argument*

$$\text{Cosh } ix = \cos x \qquad \text{Sinh } ix = i \sin x$$

$$\text{Tanh } ix = i \tan x \qquad \text{Coth } ix = -i \cot x$$

5. *Addition theorems*

$$\text{Cosh } (x \pm y) = \text{Cosh } x \text{ Cosh } y \pm \text{Sinh } x \text{ Sinh } y$$

$$\text{Sinh } (x \pm y) = \text{Sinh } x \text{ Cosh } y \pm \text{Cosh } x \text{ Sinh } y$$

$$\text{Tanh } (x \pm y) = \frac{\text{Tanh } x \pm \text{Tanh } y}{1 \pm \text{Tanh } x \text{ Tanh } y}$$

$$\text{Coth } (x \pm y) = \frac{\text{Coth } x \text{ Coth } y \pm 1}{\text{Coth } y \pm \text{Coth } x}$$

6.   *Double argument and half argument*

$$\cos 2x = \cos^2 x - \sin^2 x = 2 \cos^2 x - 1 = 1 - 2 \sin^2 x$$

$$\sin 2x = 2 \cos x \sin x$$

$$\tan 2x = \frac{2 \tan x}{1 - \tan^2 x} \qquad \cot 2x = \frac{\cot^2 x - 1}{2 \cot x}$$

$$\cos \frac{x}{2} = \sqrt{\frac{1 + \cos x}{2}} \qquad \sin \frac{x}{2} = \sqrt{\frac{1 - \cos x}{2}}$$

$$\tan \frac{x}{2} = \frac{\sin x}{1 + \cos x} = \frac{1 - \cos x}{\sin x}$$

7.   *Sum and product of two functions*

$$\cos x + \cos y = 2 \cos \frac{x + y}{2} \cos \frac{x - y}{2}$$

$$\cos x - \cos y = - 2 \sin \frac{x + y}{2} \sin \frac{x - y}{2}$$

$$\sin x \pm \sin y = 2 \sin \frac{x \pm y}{2} \cos \frac{x \mp y}{2}$$

$$\tan x \pm \tan y = \frac{\sin (x \pm y)}{\cos x \cos y}$$

$$\cot x \pm \cot y = \frac{\sin (y \pm x)}{\sin x \sin y}$$

$$2 \cos x \cos y = \cos (x - y) + \cos (x + y)$$

$$2 \sin x \sin y = \cos (x - y) - \cos (x + y)$$

$$2 \cos x \sin y = - \sin (x - y) + \sin (x + y)$$

8.   *Derivatives*

$$\frac{d \cos x}{dx} = - \sin x \qquad \frac{d \sin x}{dx} = \cos x$$

$$\frac{d \tan x}{dx} = \frac{1}{\cos^2 x} \qquad \frac{d \cot x}{dx} = - \frac{1}{\sin^2 x}$$

9.   *Integrals*

$$\int \cos x \, dx = \sin x \qquad\qquad \int \sin x \, dx = - \cos x$$

$$\int \tan x \, dx = - \ln \cos x \qquad \int \cot x \, dx = \ln \sin x$$

$$\int x \cos x \, dx = x \sin x + \cos x$$

$$\int x \sin x \, dx = - x \cos x + \sin x$$

6. Double argument and half argument

$\text{Cosh } 2x = \text{Cosh}^2 x + \text{Sinh}^2 x = 2 \text{ Cosh}^2 x - 1 = 1 + \text{Sinh}^2 x$

$\text{Sinh } 2x = 2 \text{ Cosh } x \text{ Sinh } x$

$$\text{Tanh } 2x = \frac{2 \text{ Tanh } x}{1 + \text{Tanh}^2 x} \qquad \text{Coth } 2x = \frac{\text{Coth}^2 x - 1}{2 \text{ Coth } x}$$

$$\text{Cosh } \frac{x}{2} = \sqrt{\frac{\text{Cosh } x + 1}{2}} \qquad \text{Sinh } \frac{x}{2} = \sqrt{\frac{\text{Cosh } x - 1}{2}}$$

$$\text{Tanh } \frac{x}{2} = \frac{\text{Sinh } x}{\text{Cosh } x + 1} = \frac{\text{Cosh } x - 1}{\text{Sinh } x}$$

7. Sum and product of two functions

$$\text{Cosh } x + \text{Cosh } y = 2 \text{ Cosh } \frac{x + y}{2} \text{ Cosh } \frac{x - y}{2}$$

$$\text{Cosh } x - \text{Cosh } y = 2 \text{ Sinh } \frac{x + y}{2} \text{ Sinh } \frac{x - y}{2}$$

$$\text{Sinh } x \pm \text{Sinh } y = 2 \text{ Sinh } \frac{x \pm y}{2} \text{ Cosh } \frac{x \mp y}{2}$$

$$\text{Tanh } x \pm \text{Tanh } y = \frac{\text{Sinh } (x \pm y)}{\text{Cosh } x \text{ Cosh } y}$$

$$\text{Coth } x \pm \text{Coth } y = \frac{\text{Sinh } (y \pm x)}{\text{Sinh } x \text{ Sinh } y}$$

$2 \text{ Cosh } x \text{ Cosh } y = \text{Cosh } (x + y) + \text{Cosh } (x - y)$

$2 \text{ Sinh } x \text{ Sinh } y = \text{Cosh } (x + y) - \text{Cosh } (x - y)$

$2 \text{ Cosh } x \text{ Sinh } y = \text{Sinh } (x + y) - \text{Sinh } (x - y)$

8. Derivatives

$$\frac{d \text{ Cosh } x}{dx} = \text{Sinh } x \qquad \frac{d \text{ Sinh } x}{dx} = \text{Cosh } x$$

$$\frac{d \text{ Tanh } x}{dx} = \frac{1}{\text{Cosh}^2 x} \qquad \frac{d \text{ Coth } x}{dx} = - \frac{1}{\text{Sinh}^2 x}$$

9. Integrals

$\int \text{Cosh } x \, dx = \text{Sinh } x \qquad\qquad \int \text{Sinh } x \, dx = \text{Cosh } x$

$\int \text{Tanh } x \, dx = \ln \text{Cosh } x \qquad\quad \int \text{Coth } x \, dx = \ln \text{Sinh } x$

$\int x \text{ Cosh } x \, dx = x \text{ Sinh } x - \text{Cosh } x$

$\int x \text{ Sinh } x \, dx = x \text{ Cosh } x - \text{Sinh } x$

9. *continued*

$\int x^2 \cos x \, dx = (x^2 - 2) \sin x + 2 x \cos x$

$\int x^2 \sin x \, dx = (- x^2 + 2) \cos x + 2 x \sin x$

$\left.\begin{array}{l} \int x^{-1} \cos x \, dx = \text{Ci } x \\ \int x^{-1} \sin x \, dx = \text{Si } x \end{array}\right\}$ see p. 115.

$\int x^{-2} \cos x \, dx = - x^{-1} \cos x - \text{Si } x$

$\int x^{-2} \sin x \, dx = - x^{-1} \sin x + \text{Ci } x$

$\int \cos^2 x \, dx = \frac{1}{2} (x + \cos x \sin x)$

$\int \sin^2 x \, dx = \frac{1}{2} (x - \cos x \sin x)$

$\int \cos^3 x \, dx = \frac{1}{3} \sin x (2 + \cos^2 x)$

$\int \sin^3 x \, dx = - \frac{1}{3} \cos x (2 + \sin^2 x)$

$$\int \cos^n x \, dx = \frac{1}{n} \cos^{n-1} x \sin x + \frac{n-1}{n} \int \cos^{n-2} x \, dx$$

$$\int \sin^n x \, dx = - \frac{1}{n} \sin^{n-1} x \cos x + \frac{n-1}{n} \int \sin^{n-2} x \, dx$$

$$\int \frac{dx}{\cos x} = \ln \tan \left(\frac{x}{2} + \frac{\pi}{4}\right) \qquad \int \frac{dx}{\sin x} = \ln \tan \frac{x}{2}$$

$$\int \frac{dx}{\cos^2 x} = \tan x \qquad \int \frac{dx}{\sin^2 x} = - \cot x$$

$$\int \frac{dx}{\cos x \sin x} = \ln \tan x$$

10.   *Extreme values of the argument x*

For very small arguments use the power series (1). In the vicinity of the singularities of tan x compute cot $x = 1/\tan x$ from the table values and use then linear interpolation. For arguments $x > 10$ write the argument in degrees and make use of the periodicity of the trigonometric functions (see p. 13).

9. *continued*

$\int x^2 \operatorname{Cosh} x \, dx = (x^2 + 2) \operatorname{Sinh} x - 2 x \operatorname{Cosh} x$

$\int x^2 \operatorname{Sinh} x \, dx = (x^2 + 2) \operatorname{Cosh} x - 2 x \operatorname{Sinh} x$

$\int x^{-1} \operatorname{Cosh} x \, dx = \frac{1}{2} \left(\overline{\operatorname{Ei}} \, x + \operatorname{Ei} (- x) \right)$

$\int x^{-1} \operatorname{Sinh} x \, dx = \frac{1}{2} \left(\overline{\operatorname{Ei}} \, x - \operatorname{Ei} (- x) \right)$ see p. 115.

$\int x^{-2} \operatorname{Cosh} x \, dx = - x^{-1} \operatorname{Cosh} x + \frac{1}{2} \left(\overline{\operatorname{Ei}} \, x - \operatorname{Ei} (- x) \right)$

$\int x^{-2} \operatorname{Sinh} x \, dx = - x^{-1} \operatorname{Sinh} x + \frac{1}{2} \left(\overline{\operatorname{Ei}} \, x + \operatorname{Ei} (- x) \right)$

$\int \operatorname{Cosh}^2 x \, dx = \frac{1}{2} \left(\operatorname{Cosh} x \operatorname{Sinh} x + x \right)$

$\int \operatorname{Sinh}^2 x \, dx = \frac{1}{2} \left(\operatorname{Cosh} x \operatorname{Sinh} x - x \right)$

$\int \operatorname{Cosh}^3 x \, dx = \frac{1}{3} \operatorname{Sinh} x \left(\operatorname{Cosh}^2 x + 2 \right)$

$\int \operatorname{Sinh}^3 x \, dx = \frac{1}{3} \operatorname{Cosh} x \left(\operatorname{Sinh}^2 x - 2 \right)$

$$\int \operatorname{Cosh}^n x \, dx = \frac{1}{n} \operatorname{Cosh}^{n-1} x \operatorname{Sinh} x + \frac{n - 1}{n} \int \operatorname{Cosh}^{n-2} x \, dx$$

$$\int \operatorname{Sinh}^n x \, dx = \frac{1}{n} \operatorname{Sinh}^{n-1} x \operatorname{Cosh} x - \frac{n - 1}{n} \int \operatorname{Sinh}^{n-2} x \, dx$$

$$\int \frac{dx}{\operatorname{Cosh} x} = 2 \arctan e^x \qquad \int \frac{dx}{\operatorname{Sinh} x} = \ln \operatorname{Tanh} \frac{x}{2}$$

$$\int \frac{dx}{\operatorname{Cosh}^2 x} = \operatorname{Tanh} x \qquad \int \frac{dx}{\operatorname{Sinh}^2 x} = - \operatorname{Coth} x$$

$$\int \frac{dx}{\operatorname{Cosh} x \operatorname{Sinh} x} = \ln \operatorname{Tanh} x$$

10. *Extreme values of the argument x*

For very small arguments use the power series (1). For arguments $x > 10$ use the approximations

$$\operatorname{Cosh} x \approx \operatorname{Sinh} x \approx \tfrac{1}{2} e^x, \qquad \operatorname{Tanh} x \approx 1.0000.$$

The exponential for $x > 10$ is found as indicated on p. 29.

11.   *Bibliography for trigonometric and hyperbolic functions*

J. Peters: *Seven-Place Values of Trigonometric Functions.* Berlin, 1918, New York, 1942.

sin x, cos x with 7   dec. for $x =$ 0.000° (0.001°) 90.000°,

tan x „   7   dig.   „ $x =$ 0.000° (0.001°) 88.000°,

             „   6   „   „ $x =$ 88.000° (0.001°) 89.820°,

             „   5-4   „   „ $x =$ 89.820° (0.001°) 90.000°.

Mathematical Tables Project: *Tables of Sines and Cosines for Radian Arguments.*   1940.

sin x, cos x with 8 dec. for $x =$ 0.000 (0.001) 25.000.

Mathematical Tables Project: *Tables of Circular and Hyperbolic Sines and Cosines for Radian Arguments.*   1939.

sin x, cos x, Sinh x, Cosh x with 9 dec. for $x =$ 0.0000 (0.0001) 1.9999,

             „   9   „   „ $x =$ 0.0 (0.1) 10.0.

Mathematical Tables Project, National Bureau of Standards: *Table of Circular and Hyperbolic Tangents and Cotangents for Radian Argument.*   New York, 1943.

tan x, cot x, Tanh x, Coth x with 8 dig. for $x =$ 0.0000 (0.0001) 2.0000.

12. *Periodicity of Trigonometric Functions*

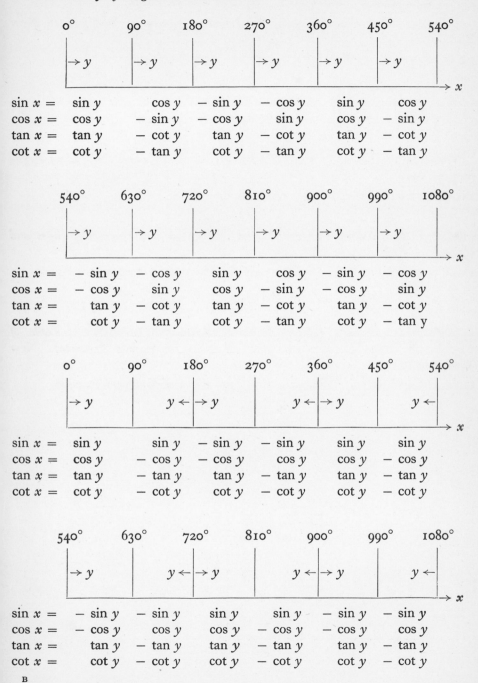

B

sin x

x	.0°	.1°	.2°	.3°	.4°	.5°	.6°	.7°	.8°	.9°	
0	.00000	0175	0349	0524	0698	0873	1047	1222	1396	1571	1745	89
1	1745	1920	2094	2269	2443	2618	2792	2967	3141	3316	3490	88
2	3490	3664	3839	4013	4188	4362	4536	4711	4885	5059	5234	87
3	5234	5408	5582	5756	5931	6105	6279	6453	6627	6802	6976	86
4	6976	7150	7324	7498	7672	7846	8020	8194	8368	8542	8716	85
5	8716	8889	9063	9237	9411	9585	9758	9932	*0106	*028	*045	84
6	.1045	063	080	097	115	132	149	167	184	201	219	83
7	219	236	253	271	288	305	323	340	357	374	392	82
8	392	409	426	444	461	478	495	513	530	547	564	81
9	564	582	599	616	633	650	668	685	702	719	736	80
10	736	754	771	788	805	822	840	857	874	891	908	79
11	908	925	942	959	977	994	*011	*028	*045	*062	*079	78
12	.2079	096	113	130	147	164	181	198	215	233	250	77
13	250	267	284	300	317	334	351	368	385	402	419	76
14	419	436	453	470	487	504	521	538	554	571	588	75
15	588	605	622	639	656	672	689	706	723	740	756	74
16	756	773	790	807	823	840	857	874	890	907	924	73
17	924	940	957	974	990	*007	*024	*040	*057	*074	*090	72
18	.3090	107	123	140	156	173	190	206	223	239	256	71
19	256	272	289	305	322	338	355	371	387	404	420	70
20	420	437	453	469	486	502	518	535	551	567	584	69
21	584	600	616	633	649	665	681	697	714	730	746	68
22	746	762	778	795	811	827	843	859	875	891	907	67
23	907	923	939	955	971	987	*003	*019	*035	*051	*067	66
24	.4067	083	099	115	131	147	163	179	195	210	226	65
25	226	242	258	274	289	305	321	337	352	368	384	64
26	384	399	415	431	446	462	478	493	509	524	540	63
27	540	555	571	586	602	617	633	648	664	679	695	62
28	695	710	726	741	756	772	787	802	818	833	848	61
29	848	863	879	894	909	924	939	955	970	985	*000	60
30	.5000	015	030	045	060	075	090	105	120	135	150	59
31	150	165	180	195	210	225	240	255	270	284	299	58
32	299	314	329	344	358	373	388	402	417	432	446	57
33	446	461	476	490	505	519	534	548	563	577	592	56
34	592	606	621	635	650	664	678	693	707	721	736	55
35	736	750	764	779	793	807	821	835	850	864	878	54
36	878	892	906	920	934	948	962	976	990	*004	*018	53
37	.6018	032	046	060	074	088	101	115	129	143	157	52
38	157	170	184	198	211	225	239	252	266	280	293	51
39	293	307	320	334	347	361	374	388	401	414	428	50
40	428	441	455	468	481	494	508	521	534	547	561	49
41	561	574	587	600	613	626	639	652	665	678	691	48
42	691	704	717	730	743	756	769	782	794	807	820	47
43	820	833	845	858	871	884	896	909	921	934	947	46
44	947	959	972	984	997	*009	*022	*034	*046	*059	*071	45
	.9°	.8°	.7°	.6°	.5°	.4°	.3°	.2°	.1°	.0°	y

cos y

sin x

x	.0°	.1°	.2°	.3°	.4°	.5°	.6°	.7°	.8°	.9°		
45	.7071	083	096	108	120	133	145	157	169	181	193	44
46	193	206	218	230	242	254	266	278	290	302	314	43
47	314	325	337	349	361	373	385	396	408	420	431	42
48	431	443	455	466	478	490	501	513	524	536	547	41
49	547	559	570	581	593	604	615	627	638	649	660	40
50	660	672	683	694	705	716	727	738	749	760	771	39
51	771	782	793	804	815	826	837	848	859	869	880	38
52	880	891	902	912	923	934	944	955	965	976	986	37
53	986	997	*007	*018	*028	*039	*049	*059	*070	*080	*090	36
54	.8090	100	111	121	131	141	151	161	171	181	192	35
55	192	202	211	221	231	241	251	261	271	281	290	34
56	290	300	310	320	329	339	348	358	368	377	387	33
57	387	396	406	415	425	434	443	453	462	471	480	32
58	480	490	499	508	517	526	536	545	554	563	572	31
59	572	581	590	599	607	616	625	634	643	652	660	30
60	660	669	678	686	695	704	712	721	729	738	746	29
61	746	755	763	771	780	788	796	805	813	821	829	28
62	829	838	846	854	862	870	878	886	894	902	910	27
63	910	918	926	934	942	949	957	965	973	980	988	26
64	988	996	*003	*011	*018	*026	*033	*041	*048	*056	*063	25
65	.9063	070	078	085	092	100	107	114	121	128	135	24
66	135	143	150	157	164	171	178	184	191	198	205	23
67	205	212	219	225	232	239	245	252	259	265	272	22
68	272	278	285	291	298	304	311	317	323	330	336	21
69	336	342	348	354	361	367	373	379	385	391	397	20
70	397	403	409	415	421	426	432	438	444	449	455	19
71	455	461	466	472	478	483	489	494	500	505	511	18
72	511	516	521	527	532	537	542	548	553	558	563	17
73	563	568	573	578	583	588	593	598	603	608	613	16
74	613	617	622	627	632	636	641	646	650	655	659	15
75	659	664	668	673	677	681	686	690	694	699	703	14
76	703	707	711	715	720	724	728	732	736	740	744	13
77	744	748	751	755	759	763	767	770	774	778	781	12
78	781	785	789	792	796	799	803	806	810	813	816	11
79	816	820	823	826	829	833	836	839	842	845	848	10
80	848	851	854	857	860	863	866	869	871	874	877	9
81	877	880	882	885	888	890	893	895	898	900	903	8
82	903	905	907	910	912	914	917	919	921	923	925	7
83	925	928	930	932	934	936	938	940	942	943	945	6
84	945	947	949	951	952	954	956	957	959	960	962	5
85	962	963	965	966	968	969	971	972	973	974	976	4
86	976	977	978	979	980	981	982	983	984	985	986	3
87	986	987	988	989	990	990	991	992	993	993	994	2
88	994	995	995	996	996	997	997	997	998	998	998	1
89	998	999	999	999	999	*000	*000	*000	*000	*000	*000	0
		.9°	.8°	.7°	.6°	.5°	.4°	.3°	.2°	.1°	.0°	y

cos y

TRIGONOMETRIC AND HYPERBOLIC FUNCTIONS

tan x

x	.0°	.1°	.2°	.3°	.4°	.5°	.6°	.7°	.8°	.9°		
0	.00000	0175	0349	0524	0698	0873	1047	1222	1396	1571	1746	89
1	1746	1920	2095	2269	2444	2619	2793	2968	3143	3317	3492	88
2	3492	3667	3842	4016	4191	4366	4541	4716	4891	5066	5241	87
3	5241	5416	5591	5766	5941	6116	6291	6467	6642	6817	6993	86
4	6993	7168	7344	7519	7695	7870	8046	8221	8397	8573	8749	85
5	8749	8925	9101	9277	9453	9629	9805	9981	*0158	*033	*051	84
6	.1051	069	086	104	122	139	157	175	192	210	228	83
7	228	246	263	281	299	317	334	352	370	388	405	82
8	405	423	441	459	477	495	512	530	548	566	584	81
9	584	602	620	638	655	673	691	709	727	745	763	80
10	763	781	799	817	835	853	871	890	908	926	944	79
11	944	962	980	998	*016	*035	*053	*071	*089	*107	*126	78
12	.2126	144	162	180	199	217	235	254	272	290	309	77
13	309	327	345	364	382	401	419	438	456	475	493	76
14	493	512	530	549	568	586	605	623	642	661	679	75
15	679	698	717	736	754	773	792	811	830	849	867	74
16	867	886	905	924	943	962	981	*000	*019	*038	*057	73
17	.3057	076	096	115	134	153	172	191	211	230	249	72
18	249	269	288	307	327	346	365	385	404	424	443	71
19	443	463	482	502	522	541	561	581	600	620	640	70
20	640	659	679	699	719	739	759	779	799	819	839	69
21	839	859	879	899	919	939	959	979	*000	*020	*040	68
22	.4040	061	081	101	122	142	163	183	204	224	245	67
23	245	265	286	307	327	348	369	390	411	431	452	66
24	452	473	494	515	536	557	578	599	621	642	663	65
25	663	684	706	727	748	770	791	813	834	856	877	64
26	877	899	921	942	964	986	*008	*029	*051	*073	*095	63
27	.5095	117	139	161	184	206	228	250	272	295	317	62
28	317	340	362	384	407	430	452	475	498	520	543	61
29	543	566	589	612	635	658	681	704	727	750	774	60
30	774	797	820	844	867	890	914	938	961	985	*009	59
31	.6009	032	056	080	104	128	152	176	200	224	249	58
32	249	273	297	322	346	371	395	420	445	469	494	57
33	494	519	544	569	594	619	644	669	694	720	745	56
34	745	771	796	822	847	873	899	924	950	976	*002	55
35	.7002	028	054	080	107	133	159	186	212	239	265	54
36	265	292	319	346	373	400	427	454	481	508	536	53
37	536	563	590	618	646	673	701	729	757	785	813	52
38	813	841	869	898	926	954	983	*012	*040	*069	*098	51
39	.8098	127	156	185	214	243	273	302	332	361	391	50
40	391	421	451	481	511	541	571	601	632	662	693	49
41	693	724	754	785	816	847	878	910	941	972	*004	48
42	.9004	036	067	099	131	163	195	228	260	293	325	47
43	325	358	391	424	457	490	523	556	590	623	657	46
44	657	691	725	759	793	827	861	896	930	965	*000	45
	.9°	.8°	.7°	.6°	.5°	.4°	.3°	.2°	.1°	.0°		y

cot y

tan x

x	.0°	.1°	.2°	.3°	.4°	.5°	.6°	.7°	.8°	.9°		
45	1.000	003	007	011	014	018	021	025	028	032	036	44
46	036	039	043	046	050	054	057	061	065	069	072	43
47	072	076	080	084	087	091	095	099	103	107	111	42
48	111	115	118	122	126	130	134	138	142	146	150	41
49	150	154	159	163	167	171	175	179	183	188	192	40
50	192	196	200	205	209	213	217	222	226	230	235	39
51	235	239	244	248	253	257	262	266	271	275	280	38
52	280	285	289	294	299	303	308	313	317	322	327	37
53	327	332	337	342	347	351	356	361	366	371	376	36
54	376	381	387	392	397	402	407	412	418	423	428	35
55	428	433	439	444	450	455	460	466	471	477	483	34
56	483	488	494	499	505	511	517	522	528	534	540	33
57	540	546	552	558	564	570	576	582	588	594	600	32
58	600	607	613	619	625	632	638	645	651	658	664	31
59	664	671	678	684	691	698	704	711	718	725	732	30
60	732	739	746	753	760	767	775	782	789	797	804	29
61	804	811	819	827	834	842	849	857	865	873	881	28
62	881	889	897	905	913	921	929	937	946	954	963	27
63	963	971	980	988	997	*006	*014	*023	*032	*041	*050	26
64	2.050	059	069	078	087	097	106	116	125	135	145	25
65	145	154	164	174	184	194	204	215	225	236	246	24
66	246	257	267	278	289	300	311	322	333	344	356	23
67	356	367	379	391	402	414	426	438	450	463	475	22
68	475	488	500	513	526	539	552	565	578	592	605	21
69	605	619	633	646	660	675	689	703	718	733	747	20
70	747	762	778	793	808	824	840	856	872	888	904	19
71	904	921	937	954	971	989	*006	*024	*042	*060	*078	18
72	3.078	096	115	133	152	172	191	211	230	251	271	17
73	271	291	312	333	354	376	398	420	442	465	487	16
74	487	511	534	558	582	606	630	655	681	706	732	15
75	732	758	785	812	839	867	895	923	952	981	*011	14
76	4.011	041	071	102	134	165	198	230	264	297	331	13
77	331	366	402	437	474	511	548	586	625	665	705	12
78	705	745	787	829	872	915	959	*005	*050	*097	*145	11
79	5.145	193	242	292	343	396	449	503	558	614	671	10
80	671	730	789	850	912	976	*041	*107	*174	*243	*314	9
81	6.314	386	460	535	612	691	772	855	940	*026	*115	8
82	7.115	207	300	396	495	596	700	806	916	*028	*144	7
83	8.144	264	386	513	643	777	915	*058	*205	*357	*514	6
84	9.514	677	845	*019	*20	*39	*58	*78	*99	**20	**43	5
85	10 × 1.143	166	191	216	243	271	300	330	362	395	430	4
86	430	467	506	546	589	635	683	734	789	846	908	3
87	908	974	*045	*120	*202	*290	*386	*490	*603	*727	*864	2
88	2.864	3.014	3.182	3.369	3.580	3.819	4.092	4.407	4.774	5.208	5.729	1
89	5.729	6.366	7.162	8.185	9.549	11.46	14.32	19.10	28.65	57.30	∞	0
	.9°	.8°	.7°	.6°	.5°	.4°	.3°	.2°	.1°	.0°		y

cot y

COS X

x	0	1	2	3	4	5	6	7	8	9
0.0	1.0000	000	*998	*996	*992	*988	*982	*976	*968	*960
1	0.9950	940	928	916	902	888	872	856	838	820
2	801	780	759	737	713	689	664	638	611	582
3	553	523	492	460	428	394	359	323	287	249
4	211	171	131	090	048	004	*961	*916	*870	*823
5	.8776	727	678	628	577	525	473	419	365	309
6	253	196	139	080	021	*961	*900	*838	*776	*712
7	.7648	584	518	452	385	317	248	179	109	038
8	.6967	895	822	749	675	600	524	448	372	294
9	216	137	058	*978	*898	*817	*735	*653	*570	*487
1.0	.5403	319	234	148	062	*976	*889	*801	*713	*625
1	.4536	447	357	267	176	085	*993	*902	*809	*717
2	.3624	530	436	342	248	153	058	*963	*867	*771
3	.2675	579	482	385	288	190	092	*994	*896	*798
4	.1700	601	502	403	304	205	106	006	*907	*807
5	+.0707	608	508	408	308	208	108	008	*092	*192
6	−.0292	392	492	592	691	791	891	990	*090	*189
7	−.1288	388	487	585	684	782	881	979	*077	*175
8	−.2272	369	466	563	660	756	852	948	*043	*138
9	−.3233	327	421	515	609	702	795	887	979	*070
2.0	−.4161	252	342	432	522	611	699	787	875	962
1	−.5048	135	220	305	390	474	557	640	722	804
2	885	966	*046	*125	*204	*282	*359	*436	*512	*588
3	−.6663	737	811	883	956	*027	*098	*168	*237	*306
4	−.7374	441	508	573	638	702	766	828	890	951
5	−.8011	071	130	187	244	301	356	410	464	517
6	569	620	670	720	768	816	863	908	953	998
7	−.9041	083	124	165	204	243	281	318	353	388
8	422	455	487	518	549	578	606	633	660	685
9	710	733	755	777	797	817	836	853	870	885
3.0	900	914	926	938	948	958	967	974	981	987
1	991	995	998	999	*000	*000	998	996	993	988
2	983	977	969	961	952	941	930	918	904	890
3	875	859	841	823	804	784	762	740	717	693
4	668	642	615	587	558	528	497	466	433	399
5	365	329	293	255	217	178	137	096	054	011
6	−.8968	923	877	831	783	735	686	636	585	534
7	481	428	373	318	262	206	148	090	030	*970
8	−.7910	848	786	723	659	594	529	462	395	328
9	259	190	120	050	*978	*907	*834	*761	*686	*612
4.0	−.6536	460	384	306	229	150	071	*991	*911	*830
1	−.5748	666	583	500	416	332	247	162	076	*990
2	−.4903	815	727	639	550	461	371	281	190	099
3	008	*916	*824	*731	*638	*545	*451	*357	*263	*168
4	−.3073	*978	*882	*787	*690	*594	*497	*400	*303	*206
5	−.2108	010	*912	*814	*715	*617	*518	*419	*320	*221
6	−.1122	022	*923	*823	*723	*623	*524	*424	*324	*224
7	−.0124	024	*076	*176	*276	*376	*476	*576	*676	*775
8	+.0875	975	*074	*173	*273	*372	*471	*570	*668	*767
9	.1865	963	*061	*159	*257	*354	*451	*548	*644	*741
5.0	.2837	932	*028	*123	*218	*312	*407	*500	*594	*687

sin x

x	0	1	2	3	4	5	6	7	8	9
0.0	.0000	100	200	300	400	500	600	699	799	899
1	998	*098	*197	*296	*395	*494	*593	*692	*790	*889
2	.1987	*085	*182	*280	*377	*474	*571	*667	*764	*860
3	.2955	*051	*146	*240	*335	*429	*523	*616	*709	*802
4	.3894	986	*078	*169	*259	*350	*439	*529	*618	*706
5	.4794	882	969	*055	*141	*227	*312	*396	*480	*564
6	.5646	729	810	891	972	*052	*131	*210	*288	*365
7	.6442	518	594	669	743	816	889	961	*033	*104
8	.7174	243	311	379	446	513	578	643	707	771
9	833	895	956	*016	*076	*134	*192	*249	*305	*360
1.0	.8415	468	521	573	624	674	724	772	820	866
1	912	957	*001	*044	*086	*128	*168	*208	*246	*284
2	.9320	356	391	425	458	490	521	551	580	608
3	636	662	687	711	735	757	779	799	819	837
4	854	871	887	901	915	927	939	949	959	967
5	975	982	987	992	995	998	999	*000	*000	998
6	996	992	988	982	976	969	960	951	940	929
7	917	903	889	874	857	840	822	802	782	761
8	738	715	691	666	640	613	585	556	526	495
9	463	430	396	362	326	290	252	214	174	134
2.0	093	051	008	*964	*919	*874	*827	*780	*731	*682
1	.8632	581	529	477	423	369	314	258	201	143
2	085	026	*966	*905	*843	*781	*718	*654	*589	*523
3	.7457	390	322	254	185	115	044	*973	*901	*828
4	.6755	681	606	530	454	378	300	222	144	065
5	.5985	904	823	742	660	577	494	410	325	240
6	155	069	*983	*896	*808	*720	*632	*543	*454	*364
7	.4274	183	092	001	*909	*817	*724	*631	*538	*444
8	.3350	255	161	066	*970	*875	*779	*683	*586	*489
9	.2392	295	198	100	002	*904	*806	*708	*609	*510
3.0	.1411	312	213	114	014	*915	*815	*715	*616	*516
1	.0416	316	216	116	016	*084	*184	*284	*384	*484
2	−.0584	684	783	883	982	*082	*181	*281	*380	*479
3	−.1577	676	775	873	971	*069	*167	*264	*362	*459
4	−.2555	652	748	844	940	*035	*131	*225	*320	*414
5	−.3508	601	694	787	880	971	*063	*154	*245	*335
6	−.4425	515	604	692	780	868	955	*042	*128	*213
7	−.5298	383	467	550	633	716	797	879	959	*039
8	−.6119	197	276	353	430	506	582	657	731	805
9	878	950	*021	*092	*162	*232	*301	*369	*436	*502
4.0	−.7568	633	697	761	823	885	946	*007	*066	*125
1	−.8183	240	296	352	406	460	513	565	616	666
2	716	764	812	859	905	950	994	*037	*080	*121
3	−.9162	201	240	278	315	351	386	420	453	485
4	516	546	576	604	631	658	683	708	731	754
5	775	796	816	834	852	868	884	899	912	925
6	937	948	957	966	974	981	986	991	995	997
7	999	*000	*000	998	996	993	989	983	977	970
8	962	952	942	931	919	905	891	876	860	843
9	825	805	785	764	742	719	695	670	644	617
5.0	589	560	531	500	468	435	402	367	332	295

COS X

x	0	1	2	3	4	5	6	7	8	9
5.0	.2837	932	*028	*123	*218	*312	*407	*500	*594	*687
1	.3780	872	964	*056	*147	*238	*328	*418	*508	*597
2	.4685	773	861	948	*035	*121	*206	*292	*376	*460
3	.5544	627	709	791	872	953	*033	*112	*191	*269
4	.6347	424	500	576	651	725	799	872	944	*016
5	.7087	157	226	295	363	430	497	563	628	692
6	756	818	880	942	*002	*061	*120	*178	*235	*292
7	.8347	402	456	509	561	612	662	712	761	808
8	855	901	946	991	*034	*076	*118	*158	*198	*237
9	.9275	312	348	383	417	450	482	514	544	573
6.0	602	629	656	681	706	729	752	774	794	814
1	833	850	867	883	898	911	924	936	947	957
2	965	973	980	986	991	994	997	999	*000	*000
3	999	996	993	989	984	978	971	962	953	943
4	932	920	907	892	877	861	844	826	807	787
5	766	744	721	697	672	646	619	591	563	533
6	502	471	438	405	370	335	298	261	223	184
7	144	103	061	018	*975	*930	*885	*838	*791	*743
8	.8694	644	593	542	489	436	382	327	271	215
9	157	099	040	*980	*919	*858	*796	*733	*669	*604
7.0	.7539	473	406	339	270	201	132	061	*990	*918
1	.6845	772	698	624	548	473	396	319	241	163
2	084	004	*924	*843	*761	*679	*597	*514	*430	*346
3	.5261	175	090	003	*916	*829	*741	*653	*564	*475
4	.4385	295	205	114	023	*931	*839	*746	*653	*560
5	.3466	372	278	183	088	*993	*898	*802	*706	*609
6	.2513	416	319	221	124	026	*928	*829	*731	*632
7	.1534	435	336	237	137	038	*938	*839	*739	*639
8	.0540	440	340	240	140	040	*060	*160	*260	*360
9	−.0460	560	660	759	859	959	*058	*158	*257	*356
8.0	−.1455	554	653	751	849	948	*046	*143	*241	*338
1	−.2435	532	629	725	821	917	*013	*108	*203	*297
2	−.3392	485	579	672	765	857	950	*041	*132	*223
3	−.4314	404	493	582	671	759	847	934	*021	*107
4	−.5193	278	363	447	530	614	696	778	859	940
5	−.6020	100	179	257	335	412	488	564	639	713
6	787	860	933	*004	*075	*146	*215	*284	*352	*420
7	−.7486	552	618	682	746	808	871	932	992	*052
8	−.8111	169	226	283	338	393	447	500	552	604
9	654	704	753	801	848	894	939	984	*027	*070
9.0	−.9111	152	192	231	269	306	342	377	412	445
1	477	509	539	569	597	625	652	677	702	726
2	748	770	791	811	830	848	865	880	895	909
3	922	934	945	955	964	972	979	985	990	994
4	997	999	*000	*000	999	997	994	990	985	979
5	972	964	955	945	934	922	909	895	880	864
6	847	829	810	790	769	747	725	701	676	650
7	624	596	567	538	507	476	443	410	376	340
8	304	267	229	190	150	109	068	025	*982	*937
9	−.8892	846	799	751	702	652	602	550	498	445
10.0	391	336	280	224	166	108	049	*990	*929	*868

sin x

x	0	1	2	3	4	5	6	7	8	9
5.0	−.9589	560	531	500	468	435	402	367	332	295
1	258	220	181	141	100	058	015	*971	*926	*881
2	−.8835	787	739	690	640	589	538	485	432	378
3	323	267	210	153	094	035	*975	*915	*853	*791
4	−.7728	664	599	534	468	401	333	265	196	126
5	055	*984	*912	*840	*766	*692	*618	*542	*467	*390
6	−.6313	235	156	077	*997	*917	*836	*755	*673	*590
7	−.5507	423	339	254	169	083	*996	*910	*822	*734
8	−.4646	557	468	378	288	198	107	015	*924	*831
9	−.3739	646	553	459	365	271	176	081	*986	*890
6.0	−.2794	698	602	505	408	311	213	116	018	*920
1	−.1822	723	625	526	427	328	229	129	030	*931
2	−.0831	731	631	532	432	332	232	132	032	*068
3	+.0168	268	368	468	568	668	767	867	967	*066
4	.1165	265	364	463	562	660	759	857	955	*053
5	.2151	249	346	443	540	637	733	829	925	*020
6	.3115	210	305	399	493	586	680	772	865	957
7	.4048	140	231	321	411	500	590	678	766	854
8	941	*028	*114	*200	*285	*369	*454	*537	*620	*703
9	.5784	866	946	*026	*106	*185	*263	*341	*418	*494
7.0	.6570	645	719	793	866	938	*010	*081	*151	*221
1	.7290	358	425	492	558	623	687	751	813	875
2	937	997	*057	*116	*174	*231	*287	*343	*397	*451
3	.8504	557	608	658	708	757	805	851	898	943
4	987	*030	*073	*115	*155	*195	*234	*272	*309	*345
5	.9380	414	447	480	511	542	571	599	627	654
6	679	704	728	750	772	793	812	831	849	866
7	882	897	910	923	935	946	956	965	973	980
8	985	990	994	997	999	*000	*000	999	997	994
9	989	984	978	971	963	954	944	933	921	908
8.0	894	879	863	845	827	808	789	768	746	723
1	699	674	648	621	594	565	535	505	473	441
2	407	373	338	301	264	226	187	147	106	064
3	022	*978	*934	*888	*842	*795	*747	*698	*648	*597
4	.8546	494	440	386	331	276	219	162	104	045
5	.7985	924	863	801	738	674	610	544	478	411
6	344	276	207	137	067	*996	*924	*851	*778	*704
7	.6630	554	479	402	325	247	169	090	010	*930
8	.5849	768	686	603	520	436	352	268	182	097
9	010	*923	*836	*748	*660	*571	*482	*393	*303	*212
9.0	.4121	030	*938	*846	*754	*661	*567	*474	*380	*286
1	.3191	096	001	*905	*809	*713	*617	*520	*423	*326
2	.2229	131	033	*935	*837	*739	*640	*542	*443	*344
3	.1245	145	046	*946	*847	*747	*647	*548	*448	*348
4	+.0248	148	048	*052	*152	*252	*352	*452	*552	*652
5	−.0752	851	951	*050	*150	*249	*348	*447	*546	*645
6	−.1743	842	940	*038	*136	*233	*331	*428	*525	*621
7	−.2718	814	910	*005	*100	*195	*290	*384	*478	*572
8	−.3665	758	850	942	*034	*125	*216	*307	*397	*486
9	−.4575	664	752	840	927	*014	*100	*186	*271	*356
10.0	−.5440	524	607	689	771	853	934	*014	*093	*172

tan x

x	0	1	2	3	4	5	6	7	8	9
0.0	0.0000	100	200	300	400	500	601	701	802	902
1	.1003	104	206	307	409	511	614	717	820	923
2	.2027	131	236	341	447	553	660	768	876	984
3	.3093	203	314	425	537	650	764	879	994	*111
4	.4228	346	466	586	708	831	954	*080	*206	*334
5	.5463	594	726	859	994	*131	*269	*410	*552	*696
6	.6841	6989	7139	7291	7445	7602	7761	7923	8087	8253
7	.8423	8595	8771	8949	9131	9316	9505	9697	9893	*0092
8	1.030	050	072	093	116	138	162	185	210	235
9	260	286	313	341	369	398	428	459	491	524
1.0	557	592	628	665	704	743	784	827	871	917
1	965	*014	*066	*120	*176	*234	*296	*360	*427	*498
2	2.572	650	733	820	912	*010	*113	*224	*341	*467
3	3.602	3.747	3.903	4.072	4.256	4.455	4.673	4.913	5.177	5.471
4	5.798	6.165	6.581	7.055	7.602	8.238	8.989	9.887	10.98	12.35
5	+14.10	16.43	19.67	24.50	32.46	48.08	92.62	1256	*108.6	*52.07
6	−34.23	25.49	20.31	16.87	14.43	12.60	11.18	10.05	9.121	8.349
7	−7.697	7.137	6.652	6.228	5.854	5.520	5.222	4.953	4.710	4.489
8	−4.286	4.100	3.929	3.771	3.624	3.488	3.361	3.242	3.130	3.026
9	−2.927	834	746	663	584	509	438	370	306	244
2.0	185	129	074	022	*973	*925	*878	*834	*791	*750
1	−1.710	671	634	598	563	529	496	464	433	403
2	374	345	318	291	264	239	214	189	165	142
3	119	097	075	054	033	0125	*9924	*9728	*9535	*9346
4	−0.9160	8978	8799	8623	8450	8280	8113	7948	7787	7627
5	−.7470	7316	7163	7013	6865	6719	6574	6432	6292	6153
6	−.6016	5881	5747	5615	5484	5354	5226	5100	4974	4850
7	−.4727	606	485	365	247	129	013	*897	*782	*668
8	−.3555	443	332	221	111	001	*893	*785	*677	*570
9	−.2464	358	253	148	044	*940	*836	*733	*630	*528
3.0	−.1425	324	222	121	019	*918	*818	*717	*617	*516
1	−.0416	316	216	116	016	*084	*184	*284	*384	*484
2	+.0585	685	786	886	987	*088	*190	*291	*393	*495
3	.1597	700	803	907	*011	*115	*219	*325	*430	*536
4	.2643	750	858	967	*076	*186	*296	*407	*519	*632
5	.3746	860	976	*092	*209	*327	*447	*567	*688	*811
6	.4935	5060	5186	5313	5442	5573	5704	5838	5973	6109
7	.6247	6387	6529	6673	6818	6966	7115	7267	7421	7577
8	.7736	7897	8060	8227	8396	8568	8743	8921	9102	9286
9	.9474	9666	9861	*0060	*026	*047	*068	*090	*112	*135
4.0	1.158	182	206	231	256	282	309	336	365	394
1	424	454	486	518	552	587	622	659	697	737
2	778	820	864	910	957	*006	*058	*111	*167	*225
3	2.286	350	416	486	560	638	719	806	897	994
4	3.096	206	322	447	580	723	878	*044	*225	*422
5	4.637	4.873	5.134	5.422	5.743	6.104	6.511	6.975	7.509	8.130
6	8.860	9.733	10.79	12.11	13.79	16.01	19.07	23.58	30.86	44.66
7	+80.71	418.6	*131.4	*56.78	*36.21	*26.58	*20.99	*17.34	*14.77	*12.86
8	−11.38	10.21	9.257	8.463	7.794	7.221	6.725	6.292	5.910	5.571
9	−5.267	4.994	4.747	4.523	4.317	4.129	3.956	3.796	3.647	3.509
.0	−3.381	3.260	3.148	3.042	2.942	2.849	2.760	2.676	2.597	2.521

tan x

x	0	1	2	3	4	5	6	7	8	9
5.0	−3.381	260	148	042	*942	*849	*760	*676	*597	*521
1	−2.449	381	316	254	194	137	083	031	*980	*932
2	−1.886	841	798	756	716	677	640	604	568	534
3	501	469	438	408	378	350	322	295	268	243
4	218	193	169	146	123	100	079	057	036	016
5	−.9956	759	565	376	189	007	*827	*651	*477	*307
6	−.8139	7975	7812	7652	7495	7340	7187	7037	6888	6742
7	−.6597	6455	6314	6175	6038	5902	5768	5635	5504	5375
8	−.5247	5120	4994	4870	4747	4625	4504	4384	4266	4148
9	−.4031	3915	3800	3686	3573	3461	3349	3238	3128	3019
6.0	−.2910	802	694	587	481	375	270	165	060	*956
1	−.1853	749	646	544	442	340	238	137	036	*935
2	−.0834	733	633	532	432	332	232	132	032	*068
3	+.0168	268	368	468	569	669	770	870	971	*072
4	.1173	275	377	479	581	684	787	890	994	*098
5	.2203	308	413	520	626	733	841	949	*058	*168
6	.3279	390	502	614	728	842	957	*073	*190	*308
7	.4428	548	669	791	915	*040	*166	*293	*422	*552
8	.5683	5816	5951	6087	6225	6365	6506	6650	6795	6942
9	.7091	7242	7396	7552	7710	7871	8034	8200	8369	8540
7.0	.8714	8892	9073	9257	9444	9635	9830	*0028	*023	*044
1	1.065	086	109	131	154	178	202	227	252	278
2	305	332	360	389	419	449	481	513	547	581
3	617	653	691	731	771	813	857	902	949	998
4	2.049	102	158	216	276	339	405	475	548	625
5	706	792	882	978	*080	*188	*303	*426	*558	*700
6	3.852	4.017	4.196	4.390	4.602	4.834	5.090	5.374	5.690	6.043
7	6.443	6.897	7.419	8.024	8.735	9.582	10.61	11.88	13.49	15.61
8	+18.51	22.72	29.42	41.69	71.52	251.2	*166.2	*62.42	*38.43	*27.75
9	−21.72	17.83	15.13	13.13	11.60	10.38	9.397	8.581	7.893	7.307
8.0	−6.800	6.357	5.968	5.622	5.314	5.036	4.785	4.557	4.349	4.158
1	−3.982	820	670	530	400	279	165	058	*958	*863
2	−2.774	689	609	533	461	392	326	263	204	146
3	091	039	*988	*940	*893	*848	*805	*763	*722	*683
4	−1.646	609	574	540	506	474	443	413	383	354
5	326	299	273	247	222	197	173	149	126	104
6	082	061	040	019	*9988	*9790	*0596	*9406	*9219	*9036
7	−.8856	8679	8505	8334	8166	8001	7838	7678	7520	7365
8	−.7211	7061	6912	6765	6620	6477	6336	6197	6059	5924
9	−.5789	656	525	395	267	140	014	*890	*766	*644
9.0	−.4523	403	284	167	050	*934	*819	*705	*591	*479
1	−.3367	256	146	036	*027	*819	*711	*604	*498	*392
2	−.2286	181	077	*973	*869	*766	*663	*560	*458	*356
3	−.1254	153	052	*951	*850	*749	*649	*548	*448	*348
4	−.0248	148	048	*052	*152	*252	*352	*453	*553	*653
5	+.0754	854	955	*056	*157	*259	*361	*463	*565	*667
6	.1770	874	977	*082	*186	*291	*397	*503	*609	*716
7	.2824	932	*041	*151	*261	*372	*484	*596	*710	*824
8	.3939	4055	4172	4290	4409	4529	4650	4772	4895	5020
9	.5146	5273	5401	5531	5662	5795	5930	6066	6203	6342
10.0	.6484	6627	6771	6918	7067	7218	7371	7527	7685	7845

Cosh x

x	0	1	2	3	4	5	6	7	8	9
0.0	1.0000	001	002	005	008	013	018	025	032	041
1	0050	061	072	085	098	113	128	145	162	181
2	0201	221	243	266	289	314	340	367	395	423
3	0453	484	516	549	584	619	655	692	731	770
4	0811	852	895	939	984	*030	*08	*12	*17	*22
5	1.128	133	138	144	149	155	161	167	173	179
6	185	192	198	205	212	219	226	233	240	248
7	255	263	271	278	287	295	303	311	320	329
8	337	346	355	365	374	384	393	403	413	423
9	433	443	454	465	475	486	497	509	520	531
1.0	543	555	567	579	591	604	616	629	642	655
1	669	682	696	709	723	737	752	766	781	796
2	811	826	841	857	872	888	905	921	937	954
3	971	988	*005	*023	*040	*058	*076	*095	*113	*132
4	2.151	170	189	209	229	249	269	290	310	331
5	352	374	395	417	439	462	484	507	530	554
6	577	601	625	650	675	700	725	750	776	802
7	828	855	882	909	936	964	992	*021	*049	*078
8	3.107	137	167	197	228	259	290	321	353	385
9	418	451	484	517	551	585	620	655	690	726
2.0	762	799	835	873	910	948	987	*026	*065	*104
1	4.144	185	226	267	309	351	393	436	480	524
2	568	613	658	704	750	797	844	891	939	988
3	5.037	087	137	188	239	290	343	395	449	503
4	557	612	667	723	780	837	895	954	*013	*072
5	6.132	193	255	317	379	443	507	571	636	702
6	769	836	904	973	*042	*112	*183	*255	*327	*400
7	7.473	548	623	699	776	853	932	*011	*091	*171
8	8.253	335	418	502	587	673	759	847	935	*024
9	9.115	206	298	391	484	579	675	772	869	968
3.0	10 × 1.007	017	027	037	048	058	069	079	090	101
1	112	123	135	146	157	169	181	192	204	216
2	229	241	253	266	279	291	304	317	331	344
3	357	371	385	399	413	427	441	456	470	485
4	500	515	530	545	561	577	592	608	625	641
5	657	674	691	708	725	742	760	777	795	813
6	831	850	868	887	906	925	944	964	984	*003
7	2.024	044	064	085	106	027	149	170	192	214
8	236	259	281	304	327	351	374	398	422	447
9	471	496	521	546	572	598	624	650	677	704
4.0	731	758	786	814	842	871	900	929	958	988
1	3.018	048	079	110	141	172	204	237	269	302
2	335	369	402	437	471	506	541	577	613	649
3	686	723	760	798	836	875	913	953	993	*033
4	4.073	114	155	197	239	282	325	368	412	457
5	501	547	592	638	685	732	780	828	876	925
6	975	*025	*075	*126	*178	*230	*282	*335	*389	*443
7	5.498	553	609	665	722	780	838	896	956	*015
8	6.076	137	199	261	324	387	452	516	582	648
9	715	782	850	919	989	*059	*130	*202	*274	*347
5.0	7.421	496	571	647	724	801	880	959	*039	*120

Sinh x

x	0	1	2	3	4	5	6	7	8	9
0.0	.0000	100	200	300	400	500	600	701	801	901
1	.1002	102	203	304	405	506	607	708	810	911
2	.2013	115	218	320	423	526	629	733	837	941
3	.3045	150	255	360	466	572	678	785	892	*000
4	.4108	216	325	434	543	653	764	875	986	*098
5	.5211	324	438	552	666	782	897	*014	*131	*248
6	.6367	6485	6605	6725	6846	6967	7090	7213	7336	7461
7	.7586	7712	7838	7966	8094	8223	8353	8484	8615	8748
8	.8881	9015	9150	9286	9423	9561	9700	9840	9981	*0122
9	1.027	041	055	070	085	099	114	129	|•145	|•160
1.0	175	191	206	222	238	254	270	286	303	319
1	336	352	369	386	403	421	438	456	474	491
2	509	528	546	564	583	602	621	640	659	679
3	698	718	738	758	779	799	820	841	862	883
4	904	926	948	970	992	*014	*037	*060	*083	*106
5	2.129	153	177	201	225	250	274	299	324	350
6	376	401	428	454	481	507	535	562	590	617
7	646	674	703	732	761	790	820	850	881	911
8	942	973	*005	*037	*069	*101	*134	*167	*200	*234
9	3.268	303	337	372	408	443	479	516	552	589
2.0	627	665	703	741	780	820	859	899	940	981
1	4.022	064	106	148	191	234	278	322	367	412
2	457	503	549	596	643	691	739	788	837	887
3	937	988	*039	*090	*142	*195	*248	*302	*356	*411
4	5.466	522	578	635	693	751	810	869	929	989
5	6.050	112	174	237	300	365	429	495	561	627
6	695	763	831	901	971	*042	*113	*185	*258	*332
7	7.406	481	557	634	711	789	868	948	*028	*110
8	8.192	275	359	443	529	615	702	790	879	969
9	9.060	151	244	337	431	527	623	720	819	918
3.0	10 × 1.002	012	022	032	043	053	064	075	086	097
1	108	119	130	142	153	165	176	188	200	212
2	225	237	249	262	275	288	301	314	327	340
3	354	367	381	395	409	423	438	452	467	482
4	497	512	527	542	558	573	589	605	621	638
5	654	671	688	705	722	739	757	774	792	810
6	829	847	866	884	903	922	942	961	981	*001
7	2.021	041	062	083	104	125	146	168	190	212
8	234	256	279	302	325	349	372	396	420	445
9	469	494	519	544	570	596	622	648	675	702
4.0	729	756	784	812	840	869	898	927	956	986
1	3.016	047	077	108	139	171	203	235	268	300
2	334	367	401	435	470	505	540	575	611	648
3	684	721	759	797	835	873	912	952	991	*031
4	4.072	113	154	196	238	281	324	367	411	456
5	500	546	591	637	684	731	779	827	875	924
6	974	*024	*074	*125	*177	*229	*281	*334	*388	*442
7	5.497	552	608	664	721	779	837	896	955	*015
8	6.075	136	198	260	323	387	451	516	581	647
9	714	782	850	919	988	*058	*129	*201	*273	*346
5.0	7.420	495	570	646	723	801	879	958	*038	*119

Cosh x ≈ Sinh x

The values given are Cosh x; a ' indicates that for Sinh x the last digit must be diminished by one unit.

x	0	1	2	3	4	5	6	7	8	9
5.0	10 ×7.421'	496'	571'	647'	724'	801	880'	959'	*039'	*120'
1	8.201	284'	367'	451	536'	622'	709'	796'	884	974'
2	9.064'	155'	247'	340'	434'	529'	624	721	819'	917
3	10²×1.002	012	022	032	043	053	064	074	085	096
4	107	118	129	141	152	164	176'	187	199	211
5	223	236	248	261	273	286	299	312	325	339
6	352	366	379	393	407	421	436	450	465	479
7	494	509	525	540	555	571	587	603	619	635
8	652'	668	685	702	719	736	754	771	789	807
9	825	844	862	881	900	919	938	958	977	997
6.0	2.017	037	058	079	099	121	142	163	185	207
1	229	252	274	297	320	344	367	391	415	439
2	464	489'	514	539	564	590	616	642	669	696
3	723	750	778	806	834	862	891	920	950	979
4	3.009	039	070	101	132	164	195	227	260	293
5	326	359	393	427	461	496	531	567	603	639
6	675	712	750	787	825	864	903	942	982	*022
7	4.062	103	144	186	228	270	313	357	400	445
8	489	534	580	626	672	719	767	815	863	912
9	961	*011	*062	*112	*164	*216	*268	*321	*375	*429
7.0	5.483	538	594	650	707	764	822	881	940	*000
1	6.060	121	182	244	307	371	435	499	565	631
2	697	764	832	901	970	*041	*111	*183	*255	*328
3	7.402'	476	551	627	704	781	859	938	*018	*099
4	8.180	262	345	429	514	599	686	773	861	950
5	9.040	131	223	316	409	504	599	696	793	892
6	991	*091	*19	*30	*40	*50	*61	*72	*82	*93
7	10³×1.104	115	126	138	149	161	172	184	196	208
8	220	233	245	257	270	283	296	309	322	335
9	349	362	376	390	404	418	432	446	461	476
8.0	490	505	521	536	551	567	583	599	615	631
1	647	664	681	697	714	732	749	767	784	802
2	820	839	857	876	895	914	933	952	972	992
3	2.012	032	053	073	094	115	136	158	180	201
4	224	246	268	291	314	338	361	385	409	433
5	457	482	507	532	558	583	609	636	662	689
6	716	743	771	799	827	855	884	913	942	972
7	3.001	032	062	093	124	155	187	219	251	284
8	317	350	384	418	452	487	522	558	593	630
9	666	703	740	778	816	854	893	932	971	*011
9.0	4.052	092	133	175	217	259	302	345	389	433
1	478	523	568	614	660	707	755	802	851	899
2	949	998	*049	*099	*151	*202	*255	*307	*361	*415
3	5.469	524	579	636	692	749	807	866	925	984
4	6.044	105	166	228	291	354	418	482	548	613
5	680	747	815	883	952	*022	*093	*164	*236	*309
6	7.382	457	532	607	684	761	839	918	997	*078
7	8.159	241	324	407	492	577	663	750	838	927
8	9.017	107	199	291	385	479	574	671	768	866
9	965	*065	*17	*27	*37	*48	*58	*69	*80	*90
10.0	10⁴×1.101	112	124	135	146	158	169	181	193	205

Tanh x

x	0	1	2	3	4	5	6	7	8	9
0.0	.0000	100	200	300	400	500	599	699	798	898
1	997	*096	*194	*293	*391	*489	*586	*684	*781	*877
2	.1974	*070	*165	*260	*355	*449	*543	*636	*729	*821
3	.2913	*004	*095	*185	*275	*364	*452	*540	*627	*714
4	.3799	885	969	*053	*136	*219	*301	*382	*462	*542
5	.4621	699	777	854	930	*005	*080	*154	*227	*299
6	.5370	441	511	581	649	717	784	850	915	980
7	.6044	107	169	231	291	351	411	469	527	584
8	640	696	751	805	858	911	963	*014	*064	*114
9	.7163	211	259	306	352	398	443	487	531	574
1.0	616	658	699	739	779	818	857	895	932	969
1	.8005	041	076	110	144	178	210	243	275	306
2	337	367	397	426	455	483	511	538	565	591
3	617	643	668	692	717	741	764	787	810	832
4	854	875	896	917	937	957	977	996	*015	*033
5	.9051	069	087	104	121	138	154	170	186	201
6	217	232	246	261	275	289	302	316	329	341
7	354	366	379	391	402	414	425	436	447	458
8	468	478	488	498	508	517	527	536	545	554
9	562	571	579	587	595	603	611	618	626	633
2.0	640	647	654	661	667	674	680	687	693	699
1	705	710	716	721	727	732	737	743	748	753
2	757	762	767	771	776	780	785	789	793	797
3	801	805	809	812	816	820	823	827	830	833
4	837	840	843	846	849	852	855	858	861	863
5	866	869	871	874	876	879	881	884	886	888
6	890	892	895	897	899	901	903	905	906	908
7	.9910	12	14	15	17	19	20	22	23	25
8	26	28	29	31	32	33	35	36	37	38
9	40	41	42	43	44	45	46	47	49	50
3.0	51	52	52	53	54	55	56	57	58	59
1	59	60	61	62	63	63	64	65	65	66
2	67	67	68	69	69	70	71	71	72	72
3	73	73	74	74	75	75	76	76	77	77
4	78	78	79	79	79	80	80	81	81	81
5	82	82	82	83	83	84	84	84	84	85
6	85	85	86	86	86	86	87	87	87	88
7	88	88	88	88	89	89	89	89	90	90
8	90	90	90	91	91	91	91	91	91	92
9	92	92	92	92	92	93	93	93	93	93
4.0	93	93	94	94	94	94	94	94	94	94
1	95	95	95	95	95	95	95	95	95	95
2	96	96	96	96	96	96	96	96	96	96
3	96	96	96	97	97	97	97	97	97	97
4	97	97	97	97	97	97	97	97	97	97
5	98	98	98	98	98	98	98	98	98	98
6	98	98	98	98	98	98	98	98	98	98
7	98	98	98	98	98	99	99	99	99	99
8	99	99	99	99	99	99	99	99	99	99
9	99	99	99	99	99	99	99	99	99	99
5.0	99	99	99	99	99	99	99	99	99	99

EXPONENTIAL FUNCTION AND LOGARITHM

Formulas

1. *Power series*

Exponential function:

$$e^x = \exp x = 1 + \frac{x}{1!} + \frac{x^2}{2!} + \frac{x^3}{3!} + \ldots \qquad -\infty < x < \infty$$

Natural logarithm:

$$\ln(1+x) = \frac{x}{1} - \frac{x^2}{2} + \frac{x^3}{3} - \frac{x^4}{4} + - \ldots \qquad -1 < x < 1$$

$$\ln\frac{1+x}{1-x} = 2\left(x + \frac{x^3}{3} + \frac{x^5}{5} + \ldots\right) \qquad -1 < x < 1$$

2. *Miscellaneous formulas*

$$\ln(e^x) = x, \qquad \exp(\ln x) = x$$

$$e^{-x} = \frac{1}{e^x}, \qquad e^x e^y = e^{x+y}, \qquad (e^x)^y = e^{xy}$$

$$\ln(x^{-1}) = -\ln x; \qquad \ln(xy) = \ln x + \ln y, \qquad \ln x^y = y \ln x$$

$$\ln(-x) = \ln x \pm i(2n+1)\pi, \text{ where } n = 0, \pm 1, \pm 2, \ldots$$

$$a^x = \exp(x \ln a)$$

3. *Common logarithm*

$$\log(10^x) = x \qquad 10^{\log x} = x$$

$$\log x = \log e \cdot \ln x, \qquad \ln x = \ln 10 \cdot \log x$$

4. *Derivatives*

$$\frac{d}{dx} e^{ax} = a e^{ax}, \qquad \frac{d}{dx} \ln ax = \frac{1}{x}$$

5. *Integrals*

$$\int e^{ax}\, dx = \frac{1}{a} e^{ax}, \qquad \int a^x\, dx = \frac{a^x}{\ln a}$$

$$\int x^n e^{ax} dx = \frac{x^n e^{ax}}{a}\left(1 - \frac{n}{a x} + \frac{n(n-1)}{a^2 x^2} - + \ldots \pm \frac{n!}{a^n x^n}\right),$$
$$n = 1, 2, 3, \ldots$$

$$\int x^{-1} e^x dx = \overline{\text{Ei}} \, x$$

$$\int e^{ax} \cos bx \, dx = \frac{e^{ax}}{a^2 + b^2}(a \cos bx + b \sin bx)$$

$$\int e^{ax} \sin bx \, dx = \frac{e^{ax}}{a^2 + b^2}(a \sin bx - b \cos bx)$$

$$\int \ln x \, dx = x(\ln x - 1)$$

$$\int x^n \ln x \, dx = \frac{x^{n+1}}{n+1}\left(\ln x - \frac{1}{n+1}\right), \qquad n \neq -1$$

$$\int \frac{\ln x}{x} dx = \frac{\ln^2 x}{n+1}$$

$$\int \frac{dx}{\ln x} = \overline{\text{Ei}}\,(\ln x)$$

$$\int \ln(a^2 + x^2) \, dx = x \ln(a^2 + x^2) - 2x - 2a \arctan \frac{a}{x}$$

$$\int x^2 \ln(a^2 + x^2) \, dx = \frac{1}{3} x^3 \ln(a^2 + x^2) - \frac{2}{9} x^3 + \frac{2}{3} a^2 x + \frac{2}{3} a^3 \arctan \frac{a}{x}$$

6. Extreme values of the argument x

Exponential function: For very small arguments use the power series (1); for $x > 10$ use the formula

$$\exp x = \left(\exp \frac{x}{n}\right)^n,$$

choosing the integer n such that x/n is in the range of the table.

Logarithm: For $x < 1$ look for $\ln(x^{-1})$. For $x > 10$ use the logarithms of the powers of 10 in conjunction with the formula

$$\ln(x \cdot 10^n) = \ln x + \ln(10^n).$$

c

7. *Bibliography*

Mathematical Tables Project: *Tables of the Exponential Function e^x.* 1939.

e^x with 18 dec. for $x = $ 0.0000 (0.0001) 1.0000,

,,   15 ,, ,, $x = $ 1.0000 (0.0001) 2.5000,

,,   15 ,, ,, $x = $ 2.500 (0.001) 5.000,

,,   12 ,, ,, $x = $ 5.00 (0.01) 10.00,

e^{-x} with 18 ,, ,, $x = $ 0.0000 (0.0001) 2.5000.

F. W. NEWMAN: *Trans. Cambridge Philos. Soc.*, vol. 13 (1883), pp. 148–241.

e^{-x} with 18 dec. for $x = $ 0.1 (0.1) 37.0,

,,   12 ,, ,, $x = $ 0.000 (0.001) 15.349,

,,   14 ,, ,, $x = $ 15.350 (0.002) 17.300,

,,   14 ,, ,, $x = $ 17.300 (0.005) 27.635.

Mathematical Tables Project: *Table of Natural Logarithms.* Vols. 1–4. 1941.

Vol. 1 : ln x with 16 dec. for $x = $ 1 (1) 50 000,

Vol. 2: ln x ,,   16 ,,   ,, $x = $ 50 000 (1) 100 000,

Vol. 3: ln x ,,   16 ,,   ,, $x = $ 0.0001 (0.0001) 5.0000,

Vol. 4: ln x ,,   16 ,,   ,, $x = $ 5.0000 (0.0001) 10.0000.

$$e^x - 1$$

x	0	1	2	3	4	5	6	7	8	9
0.00	.00000	100	200	300	401	501	602	702	803	904
.01	1005	106	207	308	410	511	613	715	816	918
.02	2020	122	224	327	429	532	634	737	840	942
.03	3045	149	252	355	458	562	666	769	873	977
.04	4081	185	289	394	498	603	707	812	917	*022
.05	5127	232	338	443	548	654	760	866	971	*078
.06	6184	290	396	503	609	716	823	930	*037	*144
.07	7251	358	466	573	681	788	896	*004	*112	*220
.08	8329	437	546	654	763	872	981	*090	*199	*308
.09	9417	527	636	746	856	966	*076	*19	*30	*41
.10	.1052	063	074	085	096	107	118	129	140	152
.11	163	174	185	196	208	219	230	241	252	264
.12	275	286	298	309	320	331	343	354	366	377
.13	388	400	411	422	434	445	457	468	480	491
.14	503	514	526	537	549	560	572	584	595	607
.15	618	630	642	653	665	677	688	700	712	723
.16	735	747	759	770	782	794	806	818	829	841
.17	853	865	877	889	901	912	924	936	948	960
.18	972	984	996	*008	*020	*032	*044	*056	*068	*080
.19	.2092	105	117	129	141	153	165	177	190	202
.20	214	226	238	251	263	275	288	300	312	324

$$1 - e^{-x}$$

x	0	1	2	3	4	5	6	7	8	9
0.00	.00000	0100	0200	0300	0399	0499	0598	0698	0797	0896
.01	0995	1094	1193	1292	1390	1489	1587	1686	1784	1882
.02	1980	2078	2176	2274	2371	2469	2566	2664	2761	2858
.03	2955	3052	3149	3246	3343	3439	3536	3632	3729	3825
.04	3921	4017	4113	4209	4305	4400	4496	4591	4687	4782
.05	4877	4972	5067	5162	5257	5351	5446	5541	5635	5729
.06	5824	5918	6012	6106	6200	6293	6387	6480	6574	6667
.07	6761	6854	6947	7040	7133	7226	7318	7411	7504	7596
.08	7688	7781	7873	7965	8057	8149	8241	8332	8424	8515
.09	8607	8698	8789	8881	8972	9063	9154	9244	9335	9426
.10	9516	9607	9697	9787	9877	9968	*0058	*015	*024	*033
.11	.1042	051	060	068	077	086	095	104	113	122
.12	131	140	149	157	166	175	184	193	201	210
.13	219	228	237	245	254	263	272	280	289	298
.14	306	315	324	332	341	350	358	367	376	384
.15	393	402	410	419	427	436	444	453	462	470
.16	479	487	496	504	513	521	530	538	546	555
.17	563	572	580	589	597	605	614	622	631	639
.18	647	656	664	672	681	689	697	706	714	722
.19	730	739	747	755	763	772	780	788	796	805
.20	813	821	829	837	845	854	862	870	878	886

e^x

x	0	1	2	3	4	5	6	7	8	9
0.0	1.000	010	020	030	041	051	062	073	083	094
1	105	116	127	139	150	162	174	185	197	209
2	221	234	246	259	271	284	297	310	323	336
3	350	363	377	391	405	419	433	448	462	477
4	492	507	522	537	553	568	584	600	616	632
5	649	665	682	699	716	733	751	768	786	804
6	822	840	859	878	896	916	935	954	974	994
7	2.014	034	054	075	096	117	138	160	181	203
8	226	248	270	293	316	340	363	387	411	435
9	460	484	509	535	560	586	612	638	664	691
1.0	718	746	773	801	829	858	886	915	945	974
1	3.004	034	065	096	127	158	190	222	254	287
2	320	353	387	421	456	490	525	561	597	633
3	669	706	743	781	819	857	896	935	975	*015
4	4.055	096	137	179	221	263	306	349	393	437
5	482	527	572	618	665	711	759	807	855	904
6	953	*003	*053	*104	*155	*207	*259	*312	*366	*419
7	5.474	529	585	641	697	755	812	871	930	989
8	6.050	110	172	234	297	360	424	488	554	619
9	686	753	821	890	959	*029	*099	*171	*243	*316
2.0	7.389	463	538	614	691	768	846	925	*004	*085
1	8.166	248	331	415	499	585	671	758	846	935
2	9.025	116	207	300	393	488	583	679	777	875
3	974	*074	*18	*28	*38	*49	*59	*70	*80	*91
4	10 × 1.102	113	125	136	147	159	170	182	194	206
5	218	230	243	255	268	281	294	307	320	333
6	346	360	374	387	401	415	430	444	459	473
7	488	503	518	533	549	564	580	596	612	628
8	644	661	678	695	712	729	746	764	781	799
9	817	836	854	873	892	911	930	949	969	989
3.0	2.009	029	049	070	091	112	133	154	176	198
1	220	242	265	287	310	334	357	381	405	429
2	453	478	503	528	553	579	605	631	658	684
3	711	739	766	794	822	850	879	908	937	967
4	996	*027	*057	*088	*119	*150	*182	*214	*246	*279
5	3.312	345	378	412	447	481	516	552	587	623
6	660	697	734	771	809	847	886	925	965	*004
7	4.045	085	126	168	210	252	295	338	382	426
8	470	515	560	606	653	699	747	794	842	891
9	940	990	*040	*091	*142	*194	*246	*298	*352	*405
4.0	5.460	515	570	626	683	740	797	856	915	974
1	6.034	095	156	218	280	343	407	472	537	602
2	669	736	803	872	941	*011	*081	*152	*224	*297
3	7.370	444	519	594	671	748	826	904	984	*064
4	8.145	227	310	393	477	563	649	736	823	912
5	9.002	092	184	276	369	463	558	654	751	849
6	948	*048	*15	*25	*35	*46	*56	*67	*78	*89
7	10^2 × 1.099	111	122	133	144	156	167	179	191	203
8	215	227	240	252	265	277	290	303	316	330
9	343	356	370	384	398	412	426	440	455	469
5.0	484	499	514	529	545	560	576	592	608	624

$$e^{-x}$$

x	0	1	2	3	4	5	6	7	8	9
0.0	1.0000	*900	*802	*704	*608	*512	*418	*324	*231	*139
1	0.9048	*958	*869	*781	*694	*607	*521	*437	*353	*270
2	.8187	106	025	*945	*866	*788	*711	*634	*558	*483
3	.7408	334	261	189	118	047	*977	*907	*839	*771
4	.6703	637	570	505	440	376	313	250	188	126
5	065	005	*945	*886	*827	*769	*712	*655	*599	*543
6	.5488	434	379	326	273	220	169	117	066	016
7	.4966	916	868	819	771	724	677	630	584	538
8	493	449	404	360	317	274	232	190	148	107
9	066	025	*985	*946	*906	*867	*829	*791	*753	*716
1.0	.3679	642	606	570	535	499	465	430	396	362
1	329	296	263	230	198	166	135	104	073	042
2	012	*982	*952	*923	*894	*865	*837	*808	*780	*753
3	.2725	698	671	645	618	592	567	541	516	491
4	466	441	417	393	369	346	322	299	276	254
5	231	209	187	165	144	122	101	080	060	039
6	019	*999	*979	*959	*940	*920	*901	*882	*864	*845
7	.1827	809	791	773	755	738	720	703	686	670
8	653	637	620	604	588	572	557	541	526	511
9	496	481	466	451	437	423	409	395	381	367
2.0	353	340	327	313	300	287	275	262	249	237
1	225	212	200	188	177	165	153	142	130	119
2	108	097	086	075	065	054	044	033	023	013
3	0026	*9926	*9827	*9730	*9633	*9537	*9442	*9348	*9255	*9163
4	$10^{-1} \times$ 0.9072	*982	*892	*804	*716	*629	*543	*458	*374	*291
5	.8208	127	046	*966	*887	*808	*730	*654	*577	*502
6	.7427	353	280	208	136	065	*995	*925	*856	*788
7	.6721	654	587	522	457	393	329	266	204	142
8	081	020	*961	*901	*843	*784	*727	*670	*613	*558
9	.5502	448	393	340	287	234	182	130	079	029
3.0	.4979	929	880	832	783	736	689	642	596	550
1	505	460	416	372	328	285	243	200	159	117
2	076	036	*996	*956	*916	*877	*839	*801	*763	*725
3	.3688	652	615	579	544	508	474	439	405	371
4	337	304	271	239	206	175	143	112	081	050
5	020	*990	*960	*930	*901	*872	*844	*816	*788	*760
6	.2732	705	678	652	625	599	573	548	522	497
7	472	448	423	399	375	352	328	305	282	260
8	237	215	193	171	149	128	107	086	065	045
9	024	004	*984	*964	*945	*925	*906	*887	*869	*850
4.0	.1832	813	795	777	760	742	725	708	691	674
1	657	641	624	608	592	576	561	545	530	515
2	500	485	470	455	441	426	412	398	384	370
3	357	343	330	317	304	291	278	265	253	240
4	228	216	203	191	180	168	156	145	133	122
5	111	100	089	078	067	057	046	036	025	015
6	0052	*9952	*9853	*9755	*9658	*9562	*9466	*9372	*9279	*9187
7	$10^{-2} \times$ 0.9095	005	*915	*826	*739	*652	*566	*480	*396	*312
8	.8230	148	067	*987	*907	*828	*750	*673	*597	*521
9	.7447	372	299	227	155	083	013	*943	*874	*806
5.0	.6738	671	605	539	474	409	346	282	220	158

EXPONENTIAL FUNCTION AND LOGARITHM

$$e^x$$

x	0	1	2	3	4	5	6	7	8	9
5.0	$10^2 \times 1.484$	499	514	529	545	560	576	592	608	624
1	640	657	673	690	707	724	742	759	777	795
2	813	831	849	868	887	906	925	944	964	983
3	2.003	024	044	064	085	106	127	149	170	192
4	214	236	259	281	304	328	351	375	398	423
5	447	472	496	521	547	572	598	624	651	677
6	704	731	759	787	815	843	871	900	929	959
7	989	*019	*049	*080	*111	*142	*173	*205	*238	*270
8	3.303	336	370	404	438	472	507	542	578	614
9	650	687	724	762	799	838	876	915	954	994
6.0	4.034	075	116	157	199	241	284	327	370	414
1	459	503	549	594	641	687	734	782	830	878
2	927	977	*027	*078	*129	*180	*232	*285	*338	*392
3	5.446	500	556	612	668	725	782	841	899	959
4	6.018	079	140	202	264	327	391	455	520	585
5	651	718	786	854	923	992	*063	*134	*205	*278
6	7.351	425	499	575	651	728	806	884	963	*043
7	8.124	206	288	371	456	541	626	713	801	889
8	978	*069	*160	*252	*345	*439	*534	*629	*726	*824
9	9.923	*022	*12	*22	*33	*43	*54	*64	*75	*86
7.0	$10^3 \times 1.097$	108	119	130	141	153	164	176	188	200
1	212	224	236	249	261	274	287	300	313	326
2	339	353	366	380	394	408	422	437	451	466
3	480	495	510	525	541	556	572	588	604	620
4	636	652	669	686	703	720	737	755	772	790
5	808	826	845	863	882	901	920	939	959	978
6	998	*018	*039	*059	*080	*101	*122	*143	*165	*186
7	2.208	231	253	276	298	322	345	368	392	416
8	441	465	490	515	540	566	592	618	644	670
9	697	724	752	779	807	836	864	893	922	951
8.0	981	*011	*041	*072	*103	*134	*165	*197	*229	*262
1	3.294	328	361	395	429	463	498	533	569	605
2	641	678	715	752	790	828	866	905	944	984
3	4.024	064	105	146	188	230	273	316	359	403
4	447	492	537	583	629	675	722	770	817	866
5	915	964	*014	*064	*115	*167	*219	*271	*324	*378
6	5.432	486	541	597	653	710	768	825	884	943
7	6.003	063	124	186	248	311	374	438	503	568
8	634	701	768	836	905	974	*044	*115	*187	*259
9	7.332	406	480	555	631	708	785	864	943	*022
9.0	8.103	185	267	350	434	519	604	691	778	866
1	955	*045	*136	*228	*321	*414	*509	*605	*701	*799
2	9.897	997	*097	*20	*30	*40	*51	*61	*72	*83
3	$10^4 \times 1.094$	105	116	127	138	150	161	173	185	197
4	209	221	233	246	258	271	284	296	310	323
5	336	349	363	377	390	404	419	433	447	462
6	476	491	506	521	537	552	568	584	599	616
7	632	648	665	681	698	715	733	750	768	785
8	803	821	840	858	877	896	915	934	954	973
9	993	*013	*033	*054	*074	*095	*116	*138	*159	*181
10.0	2.203	225	247	270	293	316	339	362	386	410

$$e^{-x}$$

x	0	1	2	3	4	5	6	7	8	9
5.0	$10^{-2}\times$0.6738	671	605	539	474	409	346	282	220	158
1	097	036	*976	*917	*858	*799	*742	*685	*628	*572
2	.5517	462	407	354	300	248	195	144	092	042
3	.4992	942	893	844	796	748	701	654	608	562
4	517	472	427	383	339	296	254	211	169	128
5	087	046	006	*966	*927	*887	*849	*810	*773	*735
6	.3698	661	625	589	553	518	483	448	414	380
7	346	313	280	247	215	183	151	120	089	058
8	028	*997	*968	*938	*909	*880	*851	*823	*795	*767
9	.2739	712	685	658	632	606	580	554	529	504
6.0	479	454	430	405	382	358	334	311	288	265
1	243	221	198	177	155	133	112	091	070	050
2	029	009	*989	*969	*950	*930	*911	*892	*873	*855
3	.1836	818	800	782	764	747	729	712	695	678
4	662	645	629	612	596	581	565	549	534	519
5	503	488	474	459	444	430	416	402	388	374
6	360	347	333	320	307	294	281	268	256	243
7	231	219	207	195	183	171	159	148	136	125
8	114	103	092	081	070	059	049	038	028	018
9	0078	*9978	*9878	*9780	*9683	*9586	*9491	*9397	*9303	*9210
7.0	$10^{-3}\times$0.9119	028	*938	*849	*761	*674	*588	*502	*418	*334
1	.8251	169	088	007	*928	*849	*771	*693	*617	*541
2	.7466	392	318	245	173	102	031	*961	*892	*823
3	.6755	688	622	556	491	426	362	299	236	174
4	113	052	*991	*932	*873	*814	*757	*699	*643	*586
5	.5531	476	421	367	314	261	209	157	106	055
6	005	*955	*905	*857	*808	*760	*713	*666	*620	*574
7	.4528	483	439	394	351	307	265	222	180	139
8	097	057	016	*976	*937	*898	*859	*820	*782	*745
9	.3707	671	634	598	562	527	492	457	422	388
8.0	355	321	288	255	223	191	159	128	097	066
1	035	005	*975	*946	*916	*887	*859	*830	*802	*774
2	.2747	719	692	665	639	613	587	561	535	510
3	485	460	436	412	388	364	340	317	294	271
4	249	226	204	182	161	139	118	097	076	055
5	035	014	*994	*975	*955	*935	*916	*897	*878	*860
6	.1841	823	805	787	769	751	734	717	700	683
7	666	649	633	617	601	585	569	553	538	522
8	507	492	477	463	448	434	420	405	391	378
9	364	350	337	324	310	297	284	272	259	247
9.0	234	222	210	198	186	174	162	151	139	128
1	117	106	095	084	073	062	052	041	031	021
2	010	0003	*9904	*9805	*9708	*9611	*9516	*9421	*9327	*9234
3	$10^{-4}\times$0.9142	051	*961	*872	*784	*697	*610	*524	*440	*356
4	.8272	190	109	028	*948	*869	*791	*713	*636	*560
5	.7485	411	337	264	192	120	049	*979	*910	*841
6	.6773	705	639	573	507	443	378	315	252	190
7	128	067	007	*947	*888	*829	*771	*714	*657	*601
8	.5545	490	435	381	328	275	222	170	119	068
9	017	*968	*918	*869	*821	*773	*725	*678	*632	*586
10.0	.4540	495	450	406	362	319	276	233	191	149

ln x

x	ln x		x	ln x
10	2.3026		10^6	13.82
10^2	4.605		10^7	16.12
10^3	6.908		10^8	18.42
10^4	9.210		10^9	20.72
10^5	11.51		10^{10}	23.03

x	0	1	2	3	4	5	6	7	8	9
1.0	.0000	100	198	296	392	488	583	677	770	862
1	953	*044	*133	*222	*310	*398	*484	*570	*655	*740
2	.1823	906	989	*070	*151	*231	*311	*390	*469	*546
3	.2624	700	776	852	927	*001	*075	*148	*221	*293
4	.3365	436	507	577	646	716	784	853	920	988
5	.4055	121	187	253	318	383	447	511	574	637
6	700	762	824	886	947	*008	*068	*128	*188	*247
7	.5306	365	423	481	539	596	653	710	766	822
8	878	933	988	*043	*098	*152	*206	*259	*313	*366
9	.6419	471	523	575	627	678	729	780	831	881
2.0	931	981	*031	*080	*129	*178	*227	*275	*324	*372
1	.7419	467	514	561	608	655	701	747	793	839
2	885	930	975	*020	*065	*109	*154	*198	*242	*286
3	.8329	372	416	459	502	544	587	629	671	713
4	755	796	838	879	920	961	*002	*042	*083	*123
5	.9163	203	243	282	322	361	400	439	478	517
6	555	594	632	670	708	746	783	821	858	895
7	933	969	*006	*04	*08	*12	*15	*19	*22	*26
8	1.030	33	37	40	44	47	51	54	58	61
9	65	68	72	75	78	82	85	89	92	95
3.0	99	*02	*05	*09	*12	*15	*18	*22	*25	*28
1	1.131	35	38	41	44	47	51	54	57	60
2	63	66	69	72	76	79	82	85	88	91
3	94	97	*00	*03	*06	*09	*12	*15	*18	*21
4	1.224	27	30	33	35	38	41	44	47	50
5	53	56	58	61	64	67	70	73	75	78
6	81	84	86	89	92	95	97	*00	*03	*06
7	1.308	11	14	16	19	22	24	27	30	32
8	35	38	40	43	45	48	51	53	56	58
9	61	64	66	69	71	74	76	79	81	84
4.0	86	89	91	94	96	99	*01	*04	*06	*09
1	1.411	13	16	18	21	23	26	28	30	33
2	35	37	40	42	45	47	49	52	54	56
3	59	61	63	66	68	70	72	75	77	79
4	82	84	86	88	91	93	95	97	*00	*02
5	1.504	06	09	11	13	15	17	20	22	24
6	26	28	30	33	35	37	39	41	43	45
7	48	50	52	54	56	58	60	62	64	67
8	69	71	73	75	77	79	81	83	85	87
9	89	91	93	95	97	99	*01	*03	*05	*07
5.0	1.609	11	13	15	17	19	21	23	25	27

ln x

x	0	1	2	3	4	5	6	7	8	9
5.0	1.609	11	13	15	17	19	21	23	25	27
1	29	31	33	35	37	39	41	43	45	47
2	49	51	52	54	56	58	60	62	64	66
3	68	70	71	73	75	77	79	81	83	85
4	86	88	90	92	94	96	97	99	*01	*03
5	1.705	07	08	10	12	14	16	17	19	21
6	23	25	26	28	30	32	33	35	37	39
7	40	42	44	46	47	49	51	53	54	56
8	58	60	61	63	65	66	68	70	72	73
9	75	77	78	80	82	83	85	87	88	90
6.0	92	93	95	97	98	*00	*02	*03	*05	*07
1	1.808	10	12	13	15	16	18	20	21	23
2	25	26	28	29	31	33	34	36	37	39
3	41	42	44	45	47	48	50	52	53	55
4	56	58	59	61	63	64	66	67	69	70
5	72	73	75	76	78	79	81	83	84	86
6	87	89	90	92	93	95	96	98	99	*01
7	1.902	04	05	07	08	10	11	13	14	15
8	17	18	20	21	23	24	26	27	29	30
9	32	33	34	36	37	39	40	42	43	44
7.0	46	47	49	50	52	53	54	56	57	59
1	60	62	63	64	66	67	69	70	71	73
2	74	75	77	78	80	81	82	84	85	87
3	88	89	91	92	93	95	96	97	99	*00
4	2.001	03	04	06	07	08	10	11	12	14
5	15	16	18	19	20	22	23	24	26	27
6	28	29	31	32	33	35	36	37	39	40
7	41	43	44	45	46	48	49	50	52	53
8	54	55	57	58	59	61	62	63	64	66
9	67	68	69	71	72	73	74	76	77	78
8.0	79	81	82	83	84	86	87	88	89	91
1	92	93	94	96	97	98	99	*00	*02	*03
2	2.104	05	07	08	09	10	11	13	14	15
3	16	17	19	20	21	22	23	25	26	27
4	28	29	31	32	33	34	35	37	38	39
5	40	41	42	44	45	46	47	48	49	51
6	52	53	54	55	56	58	59	60	61	62
7	63	64	66	67	68	69	70	71	72	74
8	75	76	77	78	79	80	82	83	84	85
9	86	87	88	89	91	92	93	94	95	96
9.0	97	98	99	*01	*02	*03	*04	*05	*06	*07
1	2.208	09	10	12	13	14	15	16	17	18
2	19	20	21	22	24	25	26	27	28	29
3	30	31	32	33	34	35	36	38	39	40
4	41	42	43	44	45	46	47	48	49	50
5	51	52	53	54	55	57	58	59	60	61
6	62	63	64	65	66	67	68	69	70	71
7	72	73	74	75	76	77	78	79	80	81
8	82	83	84	85	86	87	88	89	91	92
9	93	94	95	96	97	98	99	*00	*01	*02
10.0	2.303	04	05	06	07	08	09	10	11	12

BESSEL FUNCTIONS
Formulas

1. *Power series*

Bessel functions of the first kind:

$$J_0(x) = 1 - \frac{x^2}{2^2 \cdot 1!^2} + \frac{x^4}{2^4 \cdot 2!^2} - \frac{x^6}{2^6 \cdot 3!^2} + - \ldots$$

$$J_1(x) = \frac{x}{2 \cdot 0! \cdot 1!} - \frac{x^3}{2^3 \cdot 1! \cdot 2!} + \frac{x^5}{2^5 \cdot 2! \cdot 3!} - \frac{x^7}{2^7 \cdot 3! \cdot 4!} + - \ldots$$

$$J_n(x) = \frac{x^n}{2^n} \sum_{m=0}^{\infty} \frac{(-1)^m x^{2m}}{4^m m! (m+n)!}$$

Bessel functions of the second kind:

$$Y_0(x) = \frac{2}{\pi} \ln \frac{\gamma x}{2} \cdot J_0(x) - \frac{2}{\pi} \sum_{m=1}^{\infty} \frac{(-1)^m x^{2m}}{4^m m!^2} \left(\frac{1}{1} + \frac{1}{2} + \ldots + \frac{1}{m} \right)$$

$$Y_1(x) = \frac{2}{\pi} \ln \frac{\gamma x}{2} \cdot J_1(x) - \frac{2}{\pi x} -$$

$$- \frac{1}{\pi} \sum_{m=0}^{\infty} \frac{(-1)^m x^{2m+1}}{2^{2m+1} m! (m+1)!} \left(\frac{1}{1} + \frac{1}{2} + \ldots + \frac{1}{m} + \right.$$

$$\left. + \frac{1}{1} + \frac{1}{2} + \ldots + \frac{1}{m+1} \right)$$

$$Y_n(x) = \frac{2}{\pi} \ln \frac{\gamma x}{2} \cdot J_n(x) - \frac{1}{\pi} \sum_{m=0}^{n-1} \frac{(n-m-1)!}{m!} \frac{x^{2m-n}}{2^{2m-n}} -$$

$$- \frac{1}{\pi} \sum_{m=0}^{\infty} \frac{(-1)^m x^{2m+n}}{2^{2m+n} m! (m+n)!} \left(\frac{1}{1} + \frac{1}{2} + \ldots + \frac{1}{m} + \right.$$

$$\left. + \frac{1}{1} + \frac{1}{2} + \ldots + \frac{1}{m+n} \right)$$

Definition and numerical value of γ see p. 136.

Modified Bessel functions of the first kind:

$$I_0(x) = 1 + \frac{x^2}{4 \cdot 1!^2} + \frac{x^4}{4^2 \cdot 2!^2} + \frac{x^6}{4^3 \cdot 3!^2} + \ldots$$

$$I_1(x) = \frac{x}{2 \cdot 0! \cdot 1!} + \frac{x^3}{2^3 \cdot 1! \cdot 2!} + \frac{x^5}{2^5 \cdot 2! \cdot 3!} + \dots$$

$$I_n(x) = \frac{x^n}{2^n} \sum_{m=0}^{\infty} \frac{x^{2m}}{4^m \, m! \, (m+n)!}$$

Modified Bessel functions of the second kind:

$$K_0(x) = -\ln\frac{\gamma x}{2} \cdot I_0(x) + \sum_{m=1}^{\infty} \frac{x^{2m}}{4^m \, m!} \left(\frac{1}{1} + \frac{1}{2} + \dots + \frac{1}{m} \right)$$

$$K_1(x) = \ln\frac{\gamma x}{2} \cdot I_1(x) + x^{-1} -$$

$$-\tfrac{1}{2} \sum_{m=0}^{\infty} \frac{x^{2m+1}}{2^{2m+1} \, m! \, (m+1)!} \left(\frac{1}{1} + \frac{1}{2} + \dots + \frac{1}{m} + \right.$$

$$\left. + \frac{1}{1} + \frac{1}{2} + \dots + \frac{1}{m+1} \right)$$

$$K_n(x) = (-1)^{n+1} \ln\frac{\gamma x}{2} \cdot I_n(x) + \tfrac{1}{2} \sum_{m=0}^{n-1} \frac{(n-m-1)!}{m!} \frac{(-1)^m \, x^{2m-n}}{2^{2m-n}} +$$

$$+ (-1)^n \cdot \tfrac{1}{2} \sum_{m=0}^{\infty} \frac{x^{2m+n}}{2^{2m+n} \, m! \, (m+n)!} \left(\frac{1}{1} + \frac{1}{2} + \dots + \frac{1}{m} + \right.$$

$$\left. + \frac{1}{1} + \frac{1}{2} + \dots + \frac{1}{m+n} \right)$$

2. *Asymptotic expansions*

The following series are semi-convergent. For a fixed x, the terms first decrease and then increase beyond bounds. They can only be used as far as they decrease, and their sum then represents the function for which it stands with a limited accuracy, the error tending towards zero when x increases.

Beyond the limits of the tables these expansions may be used to calculate numerical values of the functions, and often the leading term of the asymptotic series may be used alone to approximate the Bessel function.

Bessel functions:

$$J_0(x) = \sqrt{\frac{2}{\pi x}} \left[P_0(x) \cos\left(x - \frac{\pi}{4}\right) - Q_0(x) \sin\left(x - \frac{\pi}{4}\right) \right]$$

$$Y_0(x) = \sqrt{\frac{2}{\pi x}} \left[P_0(x) \sin\left(x - \frac{\pi}{4}\right) + Q_0(x) \cos\left(x - \frac{\pi}{4}\right) \right]$$

with $P_0(x) \approx 1 - \dfrac{(1 \cdot 3)^2}{2! \cdot 8^2 \cdot x^2} + \dfrac{(1 \cdot 3 \cdot 5 \cdot 7)^2}{4! \cdot 8^4 \cdot x^4} - + \cdots$

$$Q_0(x) \approx -\frac{1^2}{1! \cdot 8 \cdot x} + \frac{(1 \cdot 3 \cdot 5)^2}{3! \cdot 8^3 \cdot x^3} - + \cdots$$

$$J_1(x) = \sqrt{\frac{2}{\pi x}} \left[P_1(x) \cos\left(x - \frac{3\pi}{4}\right) - Q_1(x) \sin\left(x - \frac{3\pi}{4}\right) \right]$$

$$Y_1(x) = \sqrt{\frac{2}{\pi x}} \left[P_1(x) \sin\left(x - \frac{3\pi}{4}\right) + Q_1(x) \cos\left(x - \frac{3\pi}{4}\right) \right]$$

with $P_1(x) \approx 1 + \dfrac{1^2 \cdot 3 \cdot 5}{2! \cdot 8^2 \cdot x^2} - \dfrac{(1 \cdot 3 \cdot 5)^2 \cdot 7 \cdot 9}{4! \cdot 8^4 \cdot x^4} +$

$$+ \frac{(1 \cdot 3 \cdot 5 \cdot 7 \cdot 9)^2 \cdot 11 \cdot 13}{6! \cdot 8^6 \cdot x^6} - + \cdots$$

$$Q_1(x) \approx \frac{1 \cdot 3}{1! \, 8 \, x} - \frac{(1 \cdot 3)^2 \cdot 5 \cdot 7}{3! \cdot 8^3 \cdot x^3} + \frac{(1 \cdot 3 \cdot 5 \cdot 7)^2 \cdot 9 \cdot 11}{5! \cdot 8^5 \cdot x^5} - + \cdots$$

$$J_n(x) = \sqrt{\frac{2}{\pi x}} \left[P_n(x) \cos\left(x - \frac{(2n+1)\pi}{4}\right) - \right.$$

$$\left. - Q_n(x) \sin\left(x - \frac{(2n+1)\pi}{4}\right) \right]$$

$$Y_n(x) = \sqrt{\frac{2}{\pi x}} \left[P_n(x) \sin\left(x - \frac{(2n+1)\pi}{4}\right) + \right.$$

$$\left. + Q_n(x) \cos\left(x - \frac{(2n+1)\pi}{4}\right) \right]$$

with $P_n(x) \approx 1 - \dfrac{(4n^2 - 1^2)(4n^2 - 3^2)}{2! \cdot 8^2 \cdot x^2} +$

$$+ \frac{(4n^2 - 1^2)(4n^2 - 3^2)(4n^2 - 5^2)(4n^2 - 7^2)}{4! \cdot 8^4 \cdot x^4} - + \cdots$$

$$Q_n(x) \approx \frac{4n^2 - 1^2}{1! \cdot 8 \cdot x} - \frac{(4n^2 - 1^2)(4n^2 - 3^2)(4n^2 - 5^2)}{3! \cdot 8^3 \cdot x^3} + - \cdots$$

Modified Bessel functions:

$$I_0(x) \approx \frac{e^x}{\sqrt{2\pi x}} \left[1 + \frac{1^2}{1! \cdot 8 \cdot x} + \frac{(1 \cdot 3)^2}{2! \cdot 8^2 \cdot x^2} + \frac{(1 \cdot 3 \cdot 5)^2}{3! \cdot 8^3 \cdot x^3} + \cdots \right]$$

$$I_1(x) \approx \frac{e^x}{\sqrt{2\pi x}} \left[1 - \frac{1 \cdot 3}{1! \cdot 8 \cdot x} - \frac{1^2 \cdot 3 \cdot 5}{2! \cdot 8^2 \cdot x^2} - \frac{(1 \cdot 3)^2 \cdot 5 \cdot 7}{3! \cdot 8^3 \cdot x^3} - \right.$$
$$\left. - \frac{(1 \cdot 3 \cdot 5)^2 \cdot 7 \cdot 9}{4! \cdot 8^4 \cdot x^4} - \cdots \right]$$

$$I_n(x) \approx \frac{e^x}{\sqrt{2\pi x}} \left[1 - \frac{(4n^2 - 1^2)}{1! \cdot 8 \cdot x} + \frac{(4n^2 - 1^2)(4n^2 - 3^2)}{2! \cdot 8^2 \cdot x^2} - \right.$$
$$\left. - \frac{(4n^2 - 1^2)(4n^2 - 3^2)(4n^2 - 5^2)}{3! \cdot 8^3 \cdot x^3} + - \cdots \right]$$

$$K_0(x) \approx \sqrt{\frac{\pi}{2 x}} \, e^x \left[1 - \frac{1^2}{1! \cdot 8 \cdot x} + \frac{(1 \cdot 3)^2}{2! \cdot 8^2 \cdot x^2} - \frac{(1 \cdot 3 \cdot 5)^2}{3! \cdot 8^3 \cdot x^3} + - \cdots \right]$$

$$K_1(x) \approx \sqrt{\frac{\pi}{2 x}} \, e^x \left[1 + \frac{1 \cdot 3}{1! \cdot 8 \cdot x} - \frac{1^2 \cdot 3 \cdot 5}{2! \cdot 8^2 \cdot x^2} + \frac{(1 \cdot 3)^2 \cdot 5 \cdot 7}{3! \cdot 8^3 \cdot x^3} - \right.$$
$$\left. - \frac{(1 \cdot 3 \cdot 5)^2 \cdot 7 \cdot 9}{4! \cdot 8^4 \cdot x^4} + - \cdots \right]$$

$$K_n(x) \approx \sqrt{\frac{\pi}{2 x}} \, e^x \left[1 + \frac{4n^2 - 1^2}{1! \cdot 8 \cdot x} + \frac{(4n^2 - 1^2)(4n^2 - 3^2)}{2! \cdot 8^2 \cdot x^2} + \right.$$
$$\left. + \frac{(4n^2 - 1^2)(4n^2 - 3^2)(4n^2 - 5^2)}{3! \cdot 8^3 \cdot x^3} + \cdots \right]$$

3. *Relations between Bessel functions and modified Bessel functions*

$$J_n(ix) = i^n I_n(x)$$

$$J_0(ix) = I_0(x), \qquad J_1(ix) = i I_1(x)$$

$$Y_n(ix) = i^n \left(i I_n(x) - \frac{2}{\pi}(-1)^n K_n(x) \right)$$

$$Y_0(ix) = i I_0(x) - \frac{2}{\pi} K_0(x), \qquad Y_1(ix) = -I_1(x) + i \frac{2}{\pi} K_1(x)$$

4. *Recurrence formulas*

$$J_{n+1}(x) = -J_{n-1}(x) + \frac{2n}{x} J_n(x)$$

$$Y_{n+1}(x) = -Y_{n-1}(x) + \frac{2n}{x} Y_n(x)$$

$$I_{n+1}(x) = I_{n-1}(x) - \frac{2n}{x} I_n(x)$$

$$K_{n+1}(x) = K_{n-1}(x) + \frac{2n}{x} K_n(x)$$

5. *Derivatives*

Primes indicate differentiation with respect to the argument shown in parentheses.

$$J_n{}'(x) = J_{n-1}(x) - \frac{n}{x} J_n(x) = -J_{n+1}(x) + \frac{n}{x} J_n(x) =$$

$$= \tfrac{1}{2}(J_{n-1}(x) - J_{n+1}(x))$$

$$Y_n{}'(x) = Y_{n-1}(x) - \frac{n}{x} Y_n(x) = -Y_{n+1}(x) + \frac{n}{x} Y_n(x) =$$

$$= \tfrac{1}{2}(Y_{n-1}(x) - Y_{n+1}(x))$$

$$I_n{}'(x) = I_{n-1}(x) - \frac{n}{x} I_n(x) = I_{n+1}(x) + \frac{n}{x} I_n(x) =$$

$$= \tfrac{1}{2}(I_{n-1}(x) + I_{n+1}(x))$$

$$K_n{}'(x) = -K_{n-1}(x) - \frac{n}{x} K_n(x) = -K_{n+1}(x) + \frac{n}{x} K_n(x) =$$

$$= -\tfrac{1}{2}(K_{n-1}(x) + K_{n+1}(x))$$

$$J_0{}'(x) = -J_1(x), \qquad Y_0{}'(x) = -Y_1(x),$$

$$I_0{}'(x) = I_1(x), \qquad K_0{}'(x) = -K_1(x)$$

$$J_1{}'(x) = J_0(x) - \frac{1}{x} J_1(x) \qquad\qquad Y_1{}'(x) = Y_0(x) - \frac{1}{x} Y_1(x)$$

$$I_1{}'(x) = I_0(x) - \frac{1}{x} I_1(x) \qquad\qquad K_1{}'(x) = -K_0(x) - \frac{1}{x} K_1(x)$$

$$J_n''(x) = -\frac{1}{x} J_{n-1}(x) - \left(1 - \frac{n(n+1)}{x^2}\right) J_n(x)$$

$$Y_n''(x) = -\frac{1}{x} Y_{n-1}(x) - \left(1 - \frac{n(n+1)}{x^2}\right) Y_n(x)$$

$$I_n''(x) = -\frac{1}{x} I_{n-1}(x) + \left(1 + \frac{n(n+1)}{x^2}\right) I_n(x)$$

$$K_n''(x) = \frac{1}{x} K_{n-1}(x) + \left(1 + \frac{n(n+1)}{x^2}\right) K_n(x)$$

6. Integrals

$$\int x\, J_0(x)\, dx = x\, J_1(x) \qquad \int J_1(x)\, dx = -J_0(x)$$

$$\int x\, Y_0(x)\, dx = x\, Y_1(x) \qquad \int Y_1(x)\, dx = -Y_0(x)$$

$$\int x\, I_0(x)\, dx = x\, I_1(x) \qquad \int I_1(x)\, dx = I_0(x)$$

$$\int x\, K_0(x)\, dx = -x\, K_1(x) \qquad \int K_1(x)\, dx = -K_0(x)$$

$$\int J_n(x)\, dx = 2 \sum_{m=0}^{\infty} J_{n+2m+1}(x)$$

In the following formulas $C_n(x)$ and $\bar{C}_n(x)$ denote two general Bessel functions, i.e. linear combinations

$$C_n(x) = a\, J_n(x) + b\, Y_n(x), \qquad \bar{C}_n(x) = \bar{a}\, J_n(x) + \bar{b}\, Y_n(x)$$

with arbitrary constants $a, b, \bar{a}, \bar{b}$. With the help of the formulas of the group 3 the corresponding relations for the modified Bessel functions $I_n(x)$ and $K_n(x)$ may easily be derived.

$$\int x^{n+1} C_n(x)\, dx = x^{n+1} C_{n+1}(x)$$

$$\int x^{1-n} C_n(x)\, dx = -x^{1-n} C_{n-1}(x)$$

$$\int x\, C_n(hx)\, \bar{C}_n(kx)\, dx = (h^2 - k^2)^{-1}\, x\, [h\, C_{n+1}(hx)\, \bar{C}_n(kx) - k\, C_n(hx)\, \bar{C}_{n+1}(kx)]$$

$$\int x\, C_n(hx)\, \bar{C}_n(hx)\, dx = -\tfrac{1}{4}\, x^2\, [C_{n-1}(hx)\, \bar{C}_{n+1}(hx) - 2\, C_n(hx)\, \bar{C}_n(hx) + C_{n+1}(hx)\, \bar{C}_{n-1}(hx)]$$

$$\int x^{-1} C_m(hx)\, \bar{C}_n(hx)\, dx = (m^2 - n^2)^{-1}\, [(m-n)\, C_m(hx)\, \bar{C}_n(hx) - h\, x\, C_{m+1}(hx)\, \bar{C}_n(hx) + h\, x\, C_m(hx)\, \bar{C}_{n+1}(hx)]$$

7. Differential equations

Primes denote derivatives with respect to x; A and B are arbitrary constants.

$$x^2 y'' + xy' + (x^2 - n^2)y = 0: \qquad y = A\,J_n(x) + B\,Y_n(x)$$

$$x^2 y'' + xy' - (x^2 + n^2)y = 0: \qquad y = A\,I_n(x) + B\,K_n(x)$$

$$x^2 y'' + (1 - 2h)xy' + (k^2 x^2 + h^2 - n^2)y = 0:$$
$$y = x^h [A\,J_n(kx) + B\,Y_n(kx)]$$

8. Extreme values of the argument x

For very small arguments use the power series (1); for $x > 10$ use the asymptotic expansions (2).

9. Bibliography

E. Meissel: *Abh. Akad. Wiss.* Berlin, 1888.,
$J_0(x)$, $J_1(x)$ with 12 dec. for $x = 0.00\,(0.01)\,15.50$.
Author's notation: I_k^0, $-I_k^1$ for $J_0(k)$, $-J_1(k)$.

G. N. Watson: *A Treatise on the Theory of Bessel Functions.* Cambridge, 1922. pp. 666–713.
$J_0(x)$, $J_1(x)$, $Y_0(x)$, $Y_1(x)$
$e^{-x} I_0(x)$, $e^{-x} I_1(x)$ } with 7 dec. for $x = 0.00\,(0.02)\,16.00$.
$e^x K_0(x)$, $e^x K_1(x)$

Harvard University: *Tables of the Bessel Functions of the First Kind of Orders Zero and One.* Cambridge, Mass., 1947.
$J_0(x)$, $J_1(x)$ with 18 dec. for $x = 0.000\,(0.001)\,24.999$,
$$x = 25.00\,(0.01)\,99.99\;.$$

British Association for the Advancement of Science: *Mathematical Tables*, vol. 6. Cambridge, 1937.

$J_0(x)$, $J_1(x)$ with 10 dec. for $x = 0.000\,(0.001)\,16.000$,
$$x = 16.00\,(0.01)\,25.00\;,$$
$Y_0(x)$, $Y_1(x)$ with 8 dig. for $x = 0.00\,(0.01)\,25.00$,
$I_0(x)$, $I_1(x)$ with 9 dig. for $x = 0.000\,(0.001)\,5.000$,
$e^{-x} I_0(x)$, $e^{-x} I_1(x)$ with 8 dec. for $x = 5.00\,(0.01)\,10.00$, $10.0\,(0.1)\,20.0$,
$K_0(x)$, $K_1(x)$ with 8–9 dig. for $x = 0.00\,(0.01)\,5.00$,
$e^x K_0(x)$, $e^x K_1(x)$ with 8 dec. for $x = 5.00\,(0.01)\,10.00$, $10.0\,(0.1)\,20.0$,

9. *continued*

Mathematical Tables Project: *Table of the Bessel Functions* $J_0(z)$ *and* $J_1(z)$ *for Complex Arguments.* New York, 1943. pp. 2–21:

$J_0(x)$, $J_1(x)$ with 10 dec. for $x = 0.00\,(0.01)\,10.00$,

author's notation: $J_0(\rho\,e^{i\phi})$, $J_1(\rho\,e^{i\phi})$, real part, $\phi = 0°$, for $J_0(\rho)$, $J_1(\rho)$. pp. 362–381:

$I_0(x)$, $I_1(x)$ with 10 dec. for $x = 0.00\,(0.01)\,10.00$,

author's notation: $J_0(\rho\,e^{i\phi})$, $J_1(\rho\,e^{i\phi})$, imaginary part, $\phi = 90°$, for $I_0(\rho)$, $I_1(\rho)$.

E. Cambi: *Eleven- and Fifteen-Place Tables of Bessel Functions of the First Kind, to all Significant Orders.* New York, 1948.

$J_0(x)$, $J_1(x)$ with 11 dec. for $x = 0.00\,(0.01)\,10.50$,
$$x = 0.001\,(0.001)\,0.500.$$

D

$J_0(x)$

x	0	1	2	3	4	5	6	7	8	9
0.0	+1.0000	000	*999	*998	*996	*994	*991	*988	*984	*980
1	+0.9975	970	964	958	951	944	936	928	919	910
2	900	890	879	868	857	844	832	819	805	791
3	776	761	746	730	713	696	679	661	642	623
4	604	584	564	543	522	500	478	455	432	409
5	385	360	335	310	284	258	231	204	177	149
6	120	091	062	032	002	*971	*940	*909	*877	*845
7	+.8812	779	745	711	677	642	607	572	536	500
8	463	426	388	350	312	274	235	195	156	116
9	075	034	*993	*952	*910	*868	*825	*783	*739	*696
1.0	+.7652	608	563	519	473	428	382	336	290	243
1	196	149	101	054	006	*957	*909	*860	*810	*761
2	+.6711	661	611	561	510	459	408	356	305	253
3	201	149	096	043	*990	*937	*884	*830	*777	*723
4	+.5669	614	560	505	450	395	340	285	230	174
5	118	062	006	*950	*894	*838	*781	*725	*668	*611
6	+.4554	497	440	383	325	268	210	153	095	038
7	+.3980	922	864	806	748	690	632	574	516	458
8	400	342	284	225	167	109	051	*993	*934	*876
9	+.2818	760	702	644	586	528	470	412	354	297
2.0	239	181	124	066	009	*951	*894	*837	*780	*723
1	+.1666	609	553	496	440	383	327	271	215	159
2	104	0481	*9927	*9375	*8824	*8275	*7727	*7181	*6637	*6095
3	+.05554	5015	4478	3943	3409	2878	2348	1821	1295	0772
4	0251	*0268	*0785	*1300	*1812	*2323	*2831	*3336	*3839	*4340
5	−.04838	5334	5828	6318	6807	7292	7775	8256	8733	9208
6	9680	*0150	*062	*108	*154	*200	*245	*291	*336	*380
7	−.1424	469	512	556	599	641	684	726	768	809
8	850	891	932	972	*012	*051	*090	*129	*167	*205
9	−.2243	280	317	354	390	426	462	497	532	566
3.0	601	634	668	701	733	765	797	829	860	890
1	921	951	980	*009	*038	*066	*094	*122	*149	*176
2	−.3202	228	253	278	303	328	351	375	398	421
3	443	465	486	507	528	548	568	587	606	625
4	643	661	678	695	711	727	743	758	773	787
5	801	815	828	841	853	865	876	887	898	908
6	918	927	936	944	953	960	967	974	981	987
7	992	997	*002	*007	*011	*014	*017	*020	*022	*024
8	−.4026	027	027	028	027	027	026	025	023	021
9	018	015	012	008	004	000	*995	*990	*984	*978
4.0	−.3971	965	958	950	942	934	925	916	907	897
1	887	876	865	854	842	831	818	806	793	779
2	766	752	737	722	707	692	676	660	644	627
3	610	593	575	557	539	520	501	482	463	443
4	423	402	381	360	339	318	296	274	251	228
5	205	182	159	135	111	087	062	037	012	*987
6	−.2961	936	910	883	857	830	803	776	749	721
7	693	665	637	609	580	551	522	493	464	434
8	404	374	344	314	283	253	222	191	160	129
9	097	066	034	002	*970	*938	*906	*874	*841	*809
5.0	−.1776	743	710	677	644	611	578	544	511	477

$J_1(x)$

x	0	1	2	3	4	5	6	7	8	9
0.0	+.00000	0500	1000	1500	2000	2499	2999	3498	3997	4495
1	4994	5492	5989	6486	6983	7479	7974	8469	8964	9457
2	9950	*0442	*093	*142	*191	*240	*289	*338	*386	*435
3	+.1483	531	580	628	676	723	771	819	866	913
4	960	*007	*054	*101	*147	*194	*240	*286	*332	*377
5	+.2423	468	513	558	603	647	692	736	780	823
6	867	910	953	996	*039	*081	*124	*166	*207	*249
7	+.3290	331	372	412	452	492	532	572	611	650
8	688	727	765	803	840	878	915	951	988	*024
9	+.4059	095	130	165	200	234	268	302	335	368
1.0	401	433	465	497	528	559	590	620	650	680
1	709	738	767	795	823	850	878	904	931	957
2	983	*008	*033	*058	*082	*106	*130	*153	*176	*198
3	+.5220	242	263	284	305	325	344	364	383	401
4	419	437	455	472	488	504	520	536	551	565
5	579	593	607	620	632	644	656	667	678	689
6	699	709	718	727	735	743	751	758	765	772
7	778	783	788	793	798	802	805	808	811	813
8	815	817	818	818	819	818	818	818	817	816	814
9	812	809	806	803	799	794	790	785	779	773
2.0	767	761	754	746	738	730	721	712	703	693
1	683	672	661	650	638	626	614	601	587	574
2	560	545	530	515	500	484	468	451	434	416
3	399	381	362	343	324	305	285	265	244	223
4	202	180	158	136	113	091	067	044	020	*996
5	+.4971	946	921	895	870	843	817	790	763	736
6	708	680	652	624	595	566	536	507	477	446
7	416	385	354	323	291	260	228	195	163	130
8	097	064	030	*997	*963	*928	*894	*859	*825	*790
9	+.3754	719	683	647	611	575	538	502	465	428
3.0	391	353	316	278	240	202	164	125	087	048
1	009	*970	*931	*892	*852	*813	*773	*733	*694	*654
2	+.2613	573	533	492	452	411	370	330	289	248
3	207	165	124	083	042	000	*959	*917	*876	*834
4	+.1792	751	709	667	625	583	541	500	458	416
5	374	332	290	248	206	164	122	080	0384	*9965
6	+.09547	9128	8711	8293	7876	7459	7043	6627	6212	5797
7	5383	4970	4557	4145	3734	3323	2913	2504	2096	1688
8	1282	0877	0472	0069	*0334	*0735	*1135	*1534	*1932	*2329
9	−.02724	3119	3512	3903	4293	4682	5070	5455	5840	6223
4.0	6604	6984	7362	7739	8114	8487	8859	9229	9597	9963
1	−.10327	069	105	141	177	212	247	282	317	352
2	386	421	455	489	522	556	589	622	654	687
3	719	751	783	814	845	876	907	938	968	998
4	−.2028	057	086	115	144	173	201	229	256	284
5	311	337	364	390	416	442	467	492	517	541
6	566	589	613	636	659	682	704	726	748	770
7	791	812	832	852	872	892	911	930	949	967
8	985	*003	*020	*037	*054	*070	*086	*102	*117	*132
9	−.3147	161	175	189	202	216	228	241	253	264
5.0	276	287	298	308	318	328	337	346	355	363

$J_0(x)$

x	0	1	2	3	4	5	6	7	8	9
5.0	−.1776	743	710	677	644	611	578	544	511	477
1	443	410	376	342	308	274	240	206	171	137
2	103	069	0342	*9998	*9653	*9308	*8963	*8618	*8272	*7926
3	−.07580	7234	6888	6542	6196	5850	5504	5158	4812	4466
4	4121	3776	3431	3086	2742	2398	2054	1711	1368	1026
5	0684	0343	0003	*0337	*0677	*1015	*1353	*1690	*2027	*2362
6	+.02697	3031	3364	3696	4027	4357	4686	5014	5341	5667
7	5992	6316	6638	6959	7279	7598	7915	8231	8545	8859
8	9170	9481	9789	*0097	*040	*071	*101	*131	*161	*191
9	+.1220	250	279	308	337	366	394	423	451	479
6.0	506	534	561	589	616	642	669	695	721	747
1	773	798	824	849	873	898	922	947	970	994
2	+.2017	041	064	086	109	131	153	175	196	217
3	238	259	279	299	319	339	358	377	396	415
4	433	451	469	486	504	521	537	554	570	585
5	601	616	631	646	660	674	688	702	715	728
6	740	753	765	777	788	799	810	821	831	841
7	851	860	869	878	886	895	902	910	917	924
8	931	937	943	949	955	960	965	969	973	977
9	981	984	987	990	993	995	997	998	999	*000
7.0	+.3001	001	001	001	000	*999	*998	*997	*995	*993
1	+.2991	988	985	982	978	974	970	966	961	956
2	951	945	939	933	927	920	913	906	898	890
3	882	874	865	856	847	837	828	818	807	797
4	786	775	764	752	740	728	715	703	690	677
5	663	650	636	622	607	593	578	563	547	532
6	516	500	484	467	451	434	416	399	381	364
7	346	327	309	290	271	252	233	214	194	174
8	154	134	113	093	072	051	030	009	*987	*965
9	+.1944	922	899	877	855	832	809	786	763	740
8.0	717	693	669	645	622	597	573	549	524	500
1	475	450	425	400	375	350	325	299	274	248
2	222	196	170	144	118	092	066	039	0131	*9866
3	+.09601	9335	9068	8801	8533	8264	7996	7726	7457	7186
4	6916	6645	6373	6102	5830	5558	5285	5013	4740	4467
5	4194	3921	3648	3374	3101	2828	2554	2281	2008	1735
6	1462	1190	0917	0645	0373	0101	*0170	*0441	*0712	*0982
7	−.01252	1522	1791	2059	2327	2595	2862	3128	3394	3659
8	3923	4187	4450	4712	4974	5235	5494	5753	6012	6269
9	6525	6781	7035	7289	7541	7793	8043	8292	8540	8787
9.0	9033	9278	9522	9764	*0005	*024	*048	*072	*096	*119
1	−.1142	166	189	211	234	257	279	302	324	346
2	367	389	411	432	453	474	495	516	536	556
3	577	597	616	636	655	674	694	712	731	749
4	768	786	804	821	839	856	873	890	907	923
5	939	955	971	987	*002	*017	*032	*047	*061	*076
6	−.2090	104	117	131	144	157	169	182	194	206
7	218	230	241	252	263	273	284	294	304	313
8	323	332	341	350	358	366	374	382	389	396
9	403	410	417	423	429	434	440	445	450	455
10.0	459	464	468	471	475	478	481	484	486	488

$J_1(x)$

x	0	1	2	3	4	5	6	7	8	9
5.0	−.3276	287	298	308	318	328	337	346	355	363
1	371	379	386	393	400	406	412	417	423	428
2	432	436	440	444	447	450	453	455	457	458
3	460	460	461	461	461	461	460	459	457	456
4	453	451	448	445	442	438	434	430	425	420
5	414	409	403	396	390	383	376	368	360	352
6	343	335	325	316	306	296	286	275	264	253
7	241	230	218	205	192	179	166	153	139	125
8	110	096	081	065	050	034	018	002	*985	*969
9	−.2951	934	917	899	881	862	844	825	806	786
6.0	767	747	727	707	686	666	645	623	602	580
1	559	537	514	492	469	446	423	400	377	353
2	329	305	281	257	232	207	182	157	132	106
3	081	055	029	003	*977	*950	*924	*897	*870	*843
4	−.1816	789	762	734	707	679	651	623	595	567
5	538	510	481	453	424	395	366	337	308	279
6	250	220	191	162	132	102	073	043	0132	*9833
7	−.09534	9235	8935	8634	8333	8032	7731	7429	7127	6824
8	6522	6219	5916	5613	5310	5007	4703	4400	4097	3793
9	3490	3187	2884	2581	2279	1976	1674	1372	1071	0769
7.0	0468	0168	*0132	*0432	*0731	*1030	*1328	*1626	*1923	*2219
1	+.02515	2811	3105	3399	3692	3984	4275	4566	4856	5145
2	5433	5720	6006	6291	6575	6858	7140	7421	7701	7980
3	8257	8533	8808	9082	9355	9626	9896	*0165	*043	*070
4	+.1096	123	149	175	201	226	252	277	302	328
5	352	377	402	426	450	475	498	522	546	569
6	592	615	638	660	683	705	727	749	771	792
7	813	834	855	875	896	916	936	956	975	994
8	+.2014	032	051	069	088	106	123	141	158	175
9	192	208	225	241	257	272	287	303	317	332
8.0	346	360	374	388	401	414	427	440	452	464
1	476	488	499	510	521	531	542	552	561	571
2	580	589	598	606	614	622	630	637	644	651
3	657	664	670	675	681	686	691	696	700	704
4	708	711	715	718	720	723	725	727	729	730
5	731	732	733	733	733	733	732	731	730	729
6	728	726	724	721	719	716	713	709	705	701
7	697	693	688	683	678	672	666	660	654	648
8	641	634	626	619	611	603	595	586	577	568
9	559	550	540	530	519	509	498	487	476	465
9.0	453	441	429	417	404	391	378	365	352	338
1	324	310	296	281	267	252	237	221	206	190
2	174	158	142	125	108	091	074	057	040	022
3	004	*986	*968	*950	*931	*912	*893	*874	*855	*836
4	+.1816	797	777	757	737	716	696	675	655	634
5	613	591	570	549	527	506	484	462	440	418
6	395	373	350	328	305	282	259	236	213	190
7	166	143	119	096	072	048	025	0006	*9766	*9525
8	+.09284	9042	8799	8556	8312	8067	7822	7577	7331	7084
9	6837	6590	6342	6093	5845	5596	5347	5097	4847	4597
10.0	4347	4097	3846	3596	3345	3094	2843	2592	2341	2090

$Y_0(x)$

x	0	1	2	3	4	5	6	7	8	9
0.0	− ∞	3.005	2.564	2.305	2.122	1.979	1.863	1.764	1.678	1.602
1	−1.534	473	416	364	316	271	228	189	151	115
2	081	049	0175	*9877	*9591	*9316	*9050	*8794	*8546	*8306
3	−.8073	7847	7627	7414	7206	7003	6806	6613	6424	6240
4	−.6060	5884	5712	5542	5377	5214	5055	4898	4745	4594
5	−.4445	4299	4156	4015	3876	3739	3604	3472	3341	3212
6	−.3085	2960	2837	2715	2595	2476	2359	2244	2130	2018
7	−.1907	1797	1689	1582	1476	1372	1269	1167	1066	0966
8	−.0868	0771	0675	0580	0486	0393	0301	0210	0120	0032
9	+.0056	143	229	314	398	481	563	644	725	804
1.0	883	960	*037	*113	*188	*262	*336	*409	*480	*551
1	+.1622	691	760	828	895	961	*026	*091	*155	*218
2	+.2281	343	404	464	523	582	640	698	754	810
3	865	920	974	*027	*079	*131	*182	*232	*282	*331
4	+.3379	427	473	520	565	610	654	698	741	783
5	824	865	906	945	984	*022	*060	*097	*133	*169
6	+.4204	239	273	306	338	370	401	432	462	491
7	520	548	576	603	629	655	680	705	728	752
8	774	796	818	839	859	879	898	916	934	951
9	968	984	*000	*015	*029	*043	*056	*069	*081	*093
2.0	+.5104	114	124	133	142	150	158	165	172	177
1	183	188	192	196	199	202	204	206	207	208
2	208	207	207	205	203	201	198	194	190	186
3	181	175	169	163	156	148	141	132	123	114
4	104	094	083	072	060	048	036	022	009	*995
5	+.4981	966	951	935	919	902	885	868	850	832
6	813	794	775	755	735	714	693	672	650	628
7	605	582	559	535	511	487	462	437	411	385
8	359	333	306	279	251	223	195	167	138	109
9	079	049	019	*989	*958	*927	*896	*865	*833	*801
3.0	+.3769	736	703	670	637	603	569	535	500	466
1	431	396	361	325	289	253	217	181	144	108
2	071	033	*996	*958	*921	*883	*845	*807	*768	*730
3	+.2691	652	613	574	535	495	456	416	376	336
4	296	256	216	175	135	094	054	013	*972	*931
5	+.1890	849	808	767	726	684	643	602	560	519
6	477	436	394	352	311	269	227	186	144	102
7	061	019	*977	*936	*894	*853	*811	*769	*728	*686
8	+.0645	604	562	521	480	439	397	356	315	275
9	234	193	152	112	071	031	*009	*050	*090	*130
4.0	−.0169	209	249	288	328	367	406	445	484	522
1	561	599	638	676	714	751	789	826	864	901
2	938	974	*011	*047	*083	*119	*155	*191	*226	*261
3	−.1296	331	365	400	434	467	501	535	568	601
4	633	666	698	730	762	793	825	856	886	917
5	947	977	*007	*036	*065	*094	*123	*151	*179	*207
6	−.2235	262	289	315	342	368	394	419	444	469
7	494	518	542	566	589	612	635	658	680	702
8	723	744	765	786	806	826	845	865	884	902
9	921	939	956	973	990	*007	*023	*039	*055	*070
5.0	−.3085	100	114	128	142	155	168	180	193	204

$Y_1(x)$

x	0	1	2	3	4	5	6	7	8	9
0.0	− ∞	63.68	31.86	21.26	15.96	12.79	10.68	9.167	8.038	7.160
1	−6.459	5.886	5.409	5.007	4.662	4.364	4.103	3.873	3.670	3.487
2	−3.324	3.176	3.042	2.919	2.807	2.704	2.609	2.521	2.440	2.364
3	−2.293	227	165	107	052	000	*952	*906	*862	*820
4	−1.781	743	708	673	641	610	580	551	523	497
5	471	447	423	401	378	357	337	317	297	279
6	260	243	226	209	193	177	161	146	132	117
7	103	090	076	063	050	038	025	013	0013	*9896
8	−0.9781	669	558	449	342	236	132	030	*929	*829
9	−.8731	634	539	444	351	258	167	077	*988	*900
1.0	−.7812	726	640	555	471	388	305	223	142	061
1	−.6981	902	823	745	667	590	513	437	361	286
2	211	137	063	*990	*916	*844	*771	*699	*628	*556
3	−.5485	415	344	274	204	135	066	*997	*928	*860
4	−.4791	724	656	589	521	454	388	321	255	189
5	123	057	*992	*927	*862	*797	*732	*668	*604	*540
6	−.3476	412	349	285	222	159	096	034	*972	*909
7	−.2847	785	724	662	601	540	479	418	357	297
8	237	177	117	057	*997	*938	*879	*820	*761	*702
9	−.1644	586	528	470	412	355	297	240	184	127
2.0	070	014	*958	*902	*846	*791	*736	*681	*626	*571
1	−.0517	463	409	355	301	248	195	142	090	037
2	+.0015	067	118	170	221	272	323	373	423	473
3	523	572	621	670	719	767	815	863	911	958
4	+.1005	052	098	144	190	236	281	326	371	415
5	459	503	547	590	633	675	718	760	801	843
6	884	924	965	*005	*045	*084	*123	*162	*200	*239
7	+.2276	314	351	388	424	460	496	531	566	601
8	635	669	703	736	769	802	834	866	897	929
9	959	990	*020	*050	*079	*108	*136	*164	*192	*220
3.0	+.3247	273	300	326	351	376	401	425	449	473
1	496	519	542	564	585	607	627	648	668	688
2	707	726	745	763	780	798	815	831	847	863
3	879	893	908	922	936	949	962	975	987	999
4	+.4010	021	032	042	052	061	070	079	087	095
5	102	109	115	122	127	133	138	142	147	150
6	154	157	160	162	164	165	166	167	167	167
7	167	166	165	163	161	159	156	153	149	145
8	141	137	132	126	120	114	108	101	094	086
9	078	070	061	052	043	033	023	013	002	*991
4.0	+.3979	967	955	943	930	917	903	889	875	861
1	846	831	815	800	783	767	750	733	716	698
2	680	662	643	624	605	586	566	546	525	505
3	484	463	441	420	397	375	353	330	307	283
4	260	236	212	187	163	138	113	087	062	036
5	010	*984	*957	*930	*904	*876	*849	*821	*794	*766
6	+.2737	709	680	652	623	594	564	535	505	475
7	445	415	384	354	323	292	261	230	199	167
8	136	104	072	040	008	*976	*943	*911	*878	*845
9	+.1812	780	746	713	680	647	613	580	546	512
5.0	479	445	411	377	343	309	275	240	206	172

$$Y_0(x)$$

x	0	1	2	3	4	5	6	7	8	9
5.0	−.3085	100	114	128	142	155	168	180	193	204
1	216	227	238	249	259	269	278	287	296	304
2	313	320	328	335	341	348	354	359	365	370
3	374	379	383	386	389	392	395	397	399	400
4	402	403	403	403	403	402	402	400	399	397
5	395	392	389	386	383	379	375	370	365	360
6	354	349	342	336	329	322	315	307	299	290
7	282	273	263	254	244	233	223	212	201	189
8	177	165	153	140	127	114	101	087	073	058
9	044	029	013	*998	*982	*966	*950	*933	*916	*899
6.0	−.2882	864	846	828	810	791	772	753	734	714
1	694	674	654	633	613	592	570	549	527	505
2	483	461	438	415	393	369	346	322	299	275
3	251	226	202	177	152	127	102	077	051	025
4	−.1999	973	947	921	894	868	841	814	787	760
5	732	705	677	650	622	594	566	538	509	481
6	452	424	395	366	337	308	279	250	221	191
7	162	132	103	073	044	014	*984	*954	*924	*894
8	−.0864	834	804	774	744	714	684	653	623	593
9	563	532	502	472	441	411	381	350	320	290
7.0	259	229	199	169	139	108	078	048	018	*012
1	+.0042	072	102	131	161	191	221	250	280	309
2	339	368	397	426	455	484	513	542	571	599
3	628	656	684	713	741	769	797	824	852	879
4	907	934	961	988	*015	*042	*068	*095	*121	*147
5	+.1173	199	225	250	276	301	326	351	375	400
6	424	448	472	496	520	543	567	590	613	635
7	658	680	702	724	746	768	789	810	831	852
8	872	893	913	932	952	972	991	*010	*028	*047
9	+.2065	083	101	119	136	153	170	187	203	219
8.0	235	251	266	282	296	311	326	340	354	367
1	381	394	407	420	432	444	456	468	479	490
2	501	512	522	532	542	551	561	570	578	587
3	595	603	611	618	625	632	639	645	651	657
4	662	667	672	677	681	686	689	693	696	699
5	702	705	707	709	710	712	713	714	714	715
6	715	714	714	713	712	711	709	707	705	703
7	700	697	694	690	687	683	678	674	669	664
8	659	653	647	641	635	628	621	614	607	599
9	592	583	575	566	558	549	539	530	520	510
9.0	499	489	478	467	456	444	433	421	408	396
1	383	371	357	344	331	317	303	289	274	260
2	245	230	215	199	184	168	152	136	119	103
3	086	069	052	034	017	*999	*981	*963	*945	*926
4	+.1907	889	870	851	831	812	792	772	752	732
5	712	692	671	650	630	609	588	566	545	523
6	502	480	458	436	414	392	369	347	324	302
7	279	256	233	210	186	163	140	116	093	069
8	045	021	*998	*974	*949	*925	*901	*877	*853	*828
9	+.0804	779	755	730	705	681	656	631	606	582
10.0	557	532	507	482	457	432	407	382	357	332

$Y_1(x)$

x	0	1	2	3	4	5	6	7	8	9
5.0	+.1479	445	411	377	343	309	275	240	206	172
1	137	103	069	034	000	*965	*930	*896	*861	*827
2	+.0792	757	723	688	653	619	584	549	515	480
3	445	411	376	342	307	273	238	204	170	136
4	101	067	033	*001	*035	*069	*103	*137	*170	*204
5	−.0238	271	304	338	371	404	437	470	503	535
6	568	601	633	665	697	729	761	793	824	856
7	887	918	949	980	*011	*042	*072	*102	*133	*163
8	−.1192	222	251	281	310	339	368	396	425	453
9	481	509	536	564	591	618	645	671	698	724
6.0	750	776	801	827	852	877	902	926	950	974
1	998	*022	*045	*068	*091	*114	*136	*158	*180	*201
2	−.2223	244	265	285	306	326	346	365	385	404
3	422	441	459	477	495	512	530	547	563	580
4	596	611	627	642	657	672	686	700	714	728
5	741	754	767	779	791	803	814	826	836	847
6	857	868	877	887	896	905	913	922	930	937
7	945	952	958	965	971	977	983	988	993	997
8	−.3002	006	010	013	016	019	022	024	026	028
9	029	030	031	032	032	032	031	031	030	028
7.0	027	025	023	020	017	014	011	007	003	*999
1	−.2995	990	985	980	974	968	962	955	949	942
2	934	927	919	911	902	893	885	875	866	856
3	846	836	825	814	803	792	780	768	756	744
4	731	718	705	692	678	664	650	636	621	606
5	591	576	560	545	529	512	496	479	462	445
6	428	410	393	375	357	338	320	301	282	263
7	243	224	204	184	164	143	123	102	081	060
8	039	017	*996	*974	*952	*930	*908	*885	*863	*840
9	−.1817	794	771	748	724	701	677	653	629	605
8.0	581	556	532	507	482	457	432	407	382	357
1	331	306	280	255	229	203	177	151	125	099
2	072	046	020	*993	*967	*940	*913	*887	*860	*833
3	−.0806	779	752	725	698	671	644	617	589	562
4	535	508	480	453	426	398	371	344	316	289
5	262	234	207	180	152	125	098	071	043	016
6	+.0011	038	065	092	119	146	173	200	227	253
7	280	307	333	360	386	413	439	465	491	518
8	544	569	595	621	647	672	698	723	748	774
9	799	824	849	873	898	922	947	971	995	*019
9.0	+.1043	067	091	114	137	161	184	207	229	252
1	275	297	319	341	363	385	406	428	449	470
2	491	512	532	553	573	593	613	633	652	671
3	691	710	728	747	765	783	801	819	837	854
4	871	888	905	922	938	954	970	986	*001	*017
5	+.2032	047	061	076	090	104	118	131	145	158
6	171	183	196	208	220	232	243	254	265	276
7	287	297	307	317	326	336	345	354	362	371
8	379	387	394	402	409	416	423	429	435	441
9	447	452	458	463	467	472	476	480	484	487
10.0	490	493	496	498	500	502	504	506	507	508

BESSEL FUNCTIONS

$I_0(x)$

x	0	1	2	3	4	5	6	7	8	9
0.0	1.000	000	000	000	000	001	001	001	002	002
1	003	003	004	004	005	006	006	007	008	009
2	010	011	012	013	014	016	017	018	020	021
3	023	024	026	027	029	031	033	035	036	038
4	040	042	045	047	049	051	054	056	058	061
5	063	066	069	071	074	077	080	083	086	089
6	092	095	098	102	105	108	112	115	119	123
7	126	130	134	138	142	146	150	154	158	162
8	167	171	175	180	184	189	194	198	203	208
9	213	218	223	228	233	239	244	249	255	260
1.0	266	272	278	283	289	295	301	307	314	320
1	326	333	339	346	352	359	366	373	380	387
2	394	401	408	416	423	430	438	446	454	461
3	469	477	485	494	502	510	519	527	536	545
4	553	562	571	580	590	599	608	618	627	637
5	647	657	667	677	687	697	707	718	728	739
6	750	761	772	783	794	806	817	829	840	852
7	864	876	888	900	913	925	938	951	963	976
8	990	*003	*016	*030	*043	*057	*071	*085	*099	*113
9	2.128	142	157	172	187	202	217	233	248	264
2.0	280	296	312	328	344	361	378	395	412	429
1	446	464	482	499	517	536	554	573	591	610
2	629	648	668	687	707	727	747	768	788	809
3	830	851	872	893	915	937	959	981	*004	*026
4	3.049	072	096	119	143	167	191	215	240	265
5	290	315	341	366	392	419	445	472	499	526
6	553	581	609	637	666	694	723	752	782	812
7	842	872	903	933	965	996	*028	*060	*092	*124
8	4.157	190	224	258	292	326	361	396	431	467
9	503	539	576	613	650	688	725	764	802	841
3.0	881	921	961	*001	*042	*083	*125	*166	*209	*251
1	5.294	338	382	426	471	516	561	607	653	700
2	747	795	843	891	940	989	*039	*089	*140	*191
3	6.243	295	347	400	454	508	562	617	672	728
4	785	842	899	957	*016	*075	*134	*195	*255	*316
5	7.378	441	503	567	631	696	761	827	893	960
6	8.028	096	165	234	304	375	447	519	591	665
7	739	813	889	965	*041	*119	*197	*276	*356	*436
8	9.517	599	681	764	848	933	*019	*11	*19	*28
9	10×1.037	046	055	064	073	082	092	101	111	120
4.0	130	140	150	160	170	180	190	201	211	222
1	232	243	254	265	276	287	298	310	321	333
2	344	356	368	380	392	404	416	429	441	454
3	467	480	493	506	519	532	546	559	573	587
4	601	615	629	644	658	673	688	703	718	733
5	748	764	779	795	811	827	843	859	876	892
6	909	926	943	961	978	996	*013	*031	*049	*067
7	2.086	104	123	142	161	180	200	219	239	259
8	279	300	320	341	362	383	404	426	447	469
9	491	514	536	559	582	605	628	652	676	700
5.0	724	748	773	798	823	849	874	900	926	952

$I_1(x)$

x	0	1	2	3	4	5	6	7	8	9
0.0	.0000	050	100	150	200	250	300	350	400	450
1	501	551	601	651	702	652	803	853	904	954
2	.1005	056	107	158	209	260	311	362	414	465
3	517	569	621	673	725	777	829	882	935	987
4	.2040	093	147	200	254	307	361	415	470	524
5	579	634	689	744	800	855	911	967	*024	*080
6	.3137	194	251	309	367	425	483	542	600	659
7	719	778	838	899	959	*020	*081	*142	*204	*266
8	.4329	391	454	518	581	646	710	775	840	905
9	971	*038	*104	*171	*239	*306	*375	*443	*512	*582
1.0	.5652	722	793	864	935	*008	*080	*153	*227	*300
1	.6375	450	525	601	677	754	832	910	988	*067
2	.7147	227	308	389	470	553	636	719	803	888
3	973	*059	*146	*233	*321	*409	*498	*588	*678	*769
4	.8861	953	*046	*140	*235	*330	*426	*522	*620	*718
5	.9817	916	*017	*12	*22	*32	*43	*53	*64	*74
6	1.085	096	106	117	128	139	151	162	173	185
7	196	208	220	232	244	256	268	280	292	305
8	317	330	343	355	368	381	395	408	421	435
9	448	462	476	490	504	518	532	547	561	576
2.0	591	606	621	636	651	666	682	698	713	729
1	745	762	778	795	811	828	845	862	879	897
2	914	932	950	968	986	*004	*022	*041	*060	*079
3	2.098	117	136	156	176	196	216	236	257	277
4	298	319	340	362	383	405	427	449	471	494
5	517	540	563	586	610	633	657	682	706	731
6	755	780	806	831	857	883	909	935	962	989
7	3.016	043	071	099	127	155	184	213	242	271
8	301	331	361	392	422	453	485	516	548	580
9	613	645	678	712	745	779	813	848	883	918
3.0	953	989	*025	*062	*098	*136	*173	*211	*249	*287
1	4.326	365	405	445	485	526	567	608	650	692
2	734	777	820	864	908	953	997	*043	*088	*134
3	5.181	228	275	323	371	420	469	519	569	619
4	670	722	773	826	879	932	986	*040	*095	*150
5	6.206	262	319	376	434	493	552	611	671	732
6	793	854	917	979	*043	*107	*171	*237	*302	*369
7	7.436	503	572	640	710	780	851	922	994	*067
8	8.140	215	289	365	441	518	595	674	753	832
9	913	994	*076	*159	*242	*326	*411	*497	*584	*671
4.0	9.759	848	938	*029	*12	*21	*31	*40	*50	*59
1	10×1.069	079	088	098	108	118	129	139	149	160
2	171	181	192	203	214	225	236	248	259	271
3	282	294	306	318	330	342	354	367	379	392
4	405	417	430	444	457	470	484	497	511	525
5	539	553	567	582	596	611	626	641	656	671
6	686	702	717	733	749	765	781	798	814	831
7	848	865	882	899	917	935	952	970	988	*007
8	2.025	044	063	082	101	120	140	160	180	200
9	220	240	261	282	303	324	346	367	389	411
5.0	434	456	479	502	525	548	572	595	619	644

$I_0(x)$

x	0	1	2	3	4	5	6	7	8	9
5.0	10 × 2.724	748	773	798	823	849	874	900	926	952
1	979	*006	*033	*060	*088	*115	*143	*172	*200	*229
2	3.258	288	317	347	378	408	439	470	501	533
3	565	597	630	662	696	729	763	797	831	866
4	901	936	972	*008	*044	*081	*118	*155	*193	*231
5	4.269	308	347	387	427	467	508	549	590	632
6	674	716	759	803	846	890	935	980	*025	*071
7	5.117	164	211	259	306	355	404	453	503	553
8	604	655	707	759	811	865	918	972	*027	*082
9	6.138	194	251	308	365	424	483	542	602	662
6.0	723	785	847	910	973	*037	*102	*167	*233	*299
1	7.366	434	502	571	641	711	782	853	925	998
2	8.072	146	221	297	373	450	528	606	685	765
3	846	928	*010	*093	*177	*261	*347	*433	*520	*608
4	9.696	786	876	967	*059	*15	*25	*34	*44	*53
5	10² × 1.063	073	083	093	103	113	123	134	144	155
6	165	176	187	198	209	220	232	243	255	266
7	278	290	302	314	326	338	351	363	376	388
8	401	414	427	441	454	468	481	495	509	523
9	537	551	566	580	595	610	625	640	655	670
7.0	686	702	717	733	750	766	782	799	816	832
1	850	867	884	902	919	937	955	974	992	*010
2	2.029	048	067	086	106	126	145	165	186	206
3	227	247	268	290	311	332	354	376	398	421
4	443	466	489	513	536	560	584	608	632	657
5	682	707	732	758	783	809	836	862	889	916
6	943	971	999	*027	*055	*084	*113	*142	*171	*201
7	3.231	261	292	323	354	385	417	449	481	514
8	547	580	614	648	682	716	751	786	822	858
9	894	931	968	*005	*042	*080	*119	*157	*196	*236
8.0	4.276	316	356	397	439	480	522	565	608	651
1	695	739	784	829	874	920	966	*013	*060	*108
2	5.156	204	253	303	353	403	454	506	557	610
3	663	716	770	824	879	934	990	*047	*104	*161
4	6.219	278	337	397	457	518	580	642	705	768
5	832	896	961	*027	*093	*160	*228	*296	*365	*434
6	7.505	575	647	719	792	866	940	*015	*091	*167
7	8.244	322	401	480	561	642	723	806	889	973
8	9.058	144	230	317	406	495	584	675	767	859
9	952	*047	*14	*24	*33	*43	*53	*63	*73	*83
9.0	10³ × 1.094	104	114	125	136	146	157	168	179	190
1	202	213	225	236	248	260	272	284	296	308
2	321	333	346	359	371	384	398	411	424	438
3	451	465	479	493	507	522	536	551	565	580
4	595	610	626	641	657	673	688	704	721	737
5	753	770	787	804	821	838	856	874	891	909
6	927	946	964	983	*002	*021	*040	*060	*079	*099
7	2.119	139	159	180	201	222	243	264	286	307
8	329	352	374	397	419	442	466	489	513	537
9	561	585	610	635	660	685	711	737	763	789
10.0	16	843	870	897	925	952	981	*009	*038	*067

$I_1(x)$

x	0	1	2	3	4	5	6	7	8	9
5.0	10 × 2.434	456	479	502	525	548	572	595	619	644
1	668	693	718	743	768	794	820	846	872	899
2	925	953	980	*007	*035	*063	*092	*120	*149	*179
3	3.208	238	268	298	329	359	391	422	454	486
4	518	551	584	617	651	685	719	753	788	823
5	859	895	931	967	*004	*041	*079	*117	*155	*194
6	4.233	272	312	352	393	433	475	516	558	601
7	644	687	730	774	819	864	909	955	*001	*048
8	5.095	142	190	238	287	337	386	436	487	538
9	590	642	695	748	802	856	910	966	*021	*077
6.0	6.134	191	249	308	367	426	486	547	608	670
1	732	795	858	922	987	*053	*118	*185	*252	*320
2	7.389	458	527	598	669	741	813	886	960	*035
3	8.110	186	263	340	418	497	577	657	738	820
4	903	986	*070	*155	*241	*328	*415	*504	*593	*683
5	9.774	865	958	*051	*145	*241	*337	*434	*532	*631
6	10² × 1.073	083	093	104	114	124	135	146	156	167
7	178	189	200	212	223	235	246	258	270	282
8	294	306	318	331	343	356	369	381	394	408
9	421	434	448	461	475	489	503	517	531	546
7.0	560	575	590	605	620	635	651	666	682	698
1	714	730	746	763	779	796	813	830	847	865
2	883	900	918	936	955	973	992	*010	*029	*049
3	2.068	087	107	127	147	167	188	209	229	250
4	272	293	315	337	359	381	404	426	449	472
5	496	519	543	567	592	616	641	666	691	717
6	742	768	794	821	848	874	902	929	957	985
7	3.013	042	070	100	129	159	188	219	249	280
8	311	342	374	406	438	471	504	537	571	604
9	639	673	708	743	779	814	851	887	924	961
8.0	999	*037	*075	*114	*153	*192	*232	*272	*313	*354
1	4.395	437	479	521	564	607	651	695	740	785
2	830	876	923	969	*017	*064	*112	*161	*210	*260
3	5.310	360	411	462	514	567	620	673	727	782
4	837	892	948	*005	*062	*119	*178	*236	*296	*356
5	6.416	477	539	601	664	727	791	856	921	987
6	7.054	121	189	257	326	396	467	538	609	682
7	755	829	904	979	*055	*132	*209	*287	*366	*446
8	8.527	608	690	773	856	941	*026	*112	*199	*287
9	9.375	465	555	646	738	831	925	*020	*115	*212
9.0	10³ × 1.031	041	051	061	071	081	091	102	112	123
1	134	144	155	166	178	189	200	212	223	235
2	247	259	271	283	295	307	320	332	345	358
3	371	384	397	411	424	438	452	465	479	494
4	508	522	537	552	566	581	596	612	627	643
5	658	674	690	707	723	739	756	773	790	807
6	824	842	859	877	895	913	931	950	969	987
7	2.006	026	045	065	084	104	125	145	165	186
8	207	228	250	271	293	315	337	359	382	405
9	428	451	475	498	522	547	571	596	621	646
10.0	671	697	722	749	775	802	828	856	883	911

BESSEL FUNCTIONS

$K_0(x)$

x	0	1	2	3	4	5	6	7	8	9
0.0	∞	4.721	4.028	3.624	3.337	3.114	2.933	2.780	2.647	2.531
1	2.427	333	248	170	097	030	*967	*909	*854	*802
2	1.753	706	662	620	580	542	505	470	436	404
3	372	342	314	286	259	233	208	183	160	137
4	115	093	072	052	032	0129	*9943	*9761	*9584	*9412
5	.9244	9081	8921	8766	8614	8466	8321	8180	8042	7907
6	.7775	646	520	397	277	159	043	*930	*820	*711
7	.6605	501	399	300	202	106	012	*920	*829	*740
8	.5653	568	484	402	321	242	165	088	013	*940
9	.4867	796	727	658	591	524	459	396	333	271
1.0	210	151	092	034	*977	*922	*867	*813	*760	*707
1	.3656	605	556	507	459	411	365	319	273	229
2	185	142	100	058	017	*976	*936	*897	*858	*820
3	.2782	746	709	673	638	603	569	535	502	469
4	437	405	373	342	312	282	252	223	194	166
5	138	111	083	057	030	004	*979	*953	*928	*904
6	.1880	856	832	809	786	763	741	719	697	676
7	655	634	614	593	573	554	534	515	496	478
8	459	441	423	406	388	371	354	337	321	305
9	288	273	257	242	226	211	196	182	167	153
2.0	139	125	111	098	084	071	058	045	033	020
1	0078	*9956	*9836	*9717	*9600	*9484	*9370	*9257	*9145	*9035
2	$10^{-1} \times$ 0.8927	820	714	609	506	404	304	204	106	010
3	.7914	820	726	634	544	454	365	278	191	106
4	022	*939	*856	*775	*695	*616	*538	*461	*384	*309
5	.6235	161	089	017	*946	*877	*808	*739	*672	*606
6	.5540	475	411	348	285	223	162	102	042	*984
7	.4926	868	811	755	700	645	592	538	485	433
8	382	331	281	231	182	134	086	039	*992	*946
9	.3901	856	811	767	724	681	638	597	555	514
3.0	474	434	395	356	317	279	241	204	168	131
1	095	060	025	*990	*956	*922	*889	*856	*824	*791
2	.2759	728	697	666	636	606	576	547	518	489
3	461	433	405	378	351	325	298	272	246	221
4	196	171	146	122	098	074	051	028	005	*982
5	.1960	938	916	894	873	852	831	810	790	770
6	750	730	711	692	673	654	635	617	599	581
7	563	546	528	511	494	477	461	445	428	412
8	397	381	366	350	335	320	306	291	277	262
9	248	234	221	207	194	180	167	154	141	129
4.0	116	104	091	079	067	055	044	032	021	0092
1	$10^{-2} \times$ 0.9980	869	760	652	545	439	334	231	128	027
2	.8927	829	731	634	539	444	351	259	167	077
3	.7988	900	813	726	641	557	473	391	309	229
4	149	070	*992	*915	*839	*764	*689	*616	*543	*471
5	.6400	329	260	191	123	056	*989	*923	*858	*794
6	.5730	668	605	544	483	423	363	305	246	189
7	132	076	020	*965	*911	*857	*804	*751	*699	*648
8	.4597	547	497	448	399	351	304	257	210	164
9	119	074	030	*986	*942	*899	*857	*814	*773	*732
5.0	.3691	651	611	572	533	494	456	419	382	345

$K_1(x)$

x	0	1	2	3	4	5	6	7	8	9
0.0	$10^2 \times$ 0.	9997	4995	3327	2492	1991	1656	1417	1237	1097
1	$10^1 \times$ 0.9854	8935	8169	7519	6962	6477	6053	5678	5345	5046
2	.4776	532	309	106	*919	*747	*588	*440	*303	*175
3	.3056	*944	*839	*740	*647	*559	*476	397	*323	*252
4	.2184	120	059	001	*945	*892	*840	*792	*745	*700
5	.1656	615	575	536	499	464	429	396	364	333
6	303	274	246	219	192	167	142	118	095	072
7	050	029	0083	*9882	*9686	*9496	*9311	*9130	*8955	*8784
8	$10^0 \times$ 0.8618	456	298	144	*993	*847	*704	*564	*428	*295
9	.7165	039	*915	*794	*675	*560	*447	*336	*228	*122
1.0	.6019	*918	*819	*722	*627	*534	*443	*354	*267	*181
1	.5098	106	*935	*856	*779	*703	*629	*556	*485	*415
2	.4346	279	212	147	084	021	*960	*900	*841	*782
3	.3725	670	615	561	508	455	404	354	305	256
4	208	161	115	070	026	*982	*939	*897	*855	*814
5	.2774	734	695	657	620	583	546	510	475	440
6	406	373	340	307	275	244	213	182	152	123
7	094	065	037	009	*982	*955	*928	*902	*876	*851
8	.1826	802	777	754	730	707	684	662	640	618
9	597	575	555	534	514	494	474	455	436	417
2.0	399	380	362	345	327	310	293	276	260	244
1	227	212	196	181	166	151	136	121	107	093
2	079	065	052	038	025	0122	*9993	*9867	*9742	*9620
3	$10^{-1} \times$ 0.9498	379	261	144	029	*916	*804	*694	*586	*478
4	.8372	268	165	063	*963	*864	*767	*670	*575	*482
5	.7389	298	208	119	031	*945	*859	*775	*692	*609
6	.6528	448	369	292	215	139	064	*990	*917	*845
7	.5774	704	634	566	498	432	366	301	237	174
8	111	050	*989	*929	*869	*811	*753	*696	*639	*584
9	.4529	474	421	368	316	264	213	163	113	064
3.0	016	*968	*921	*874	*828	*782	*738	*693	*649	*606
1	.3563	521	480	438	398	358	318	279	240	202
2	164	127	090	054	018	*983	*948	*913	*879	*845
3	2812	779	746	714	682	651	620	589	559	529
4	.500	471	442	414	385	358	330	303	276	250
5	224	198	173	147	123	098	074	050	026	003
6	.1979	957	934	912	890	868	846	825	804	783
7	763	743	722	703	683	664	645	626	607	589
8	571	553	535	517	500	483	466	449	432	416
9	400	384	368	353	337	322	307	292	277	263
4.0	248	234	220	206	193	179	166	152	139	126
1	114	101	089	076	064	052	040	028	017	0052
2	$10^{-2} \times$ 0.9938	826	715	605	497	390	284	179	076	*973
3	.8872	772	674	576	479	384	290	196	104	013
4	.7923	834	746	659	573	488	404	321	239	158
5	078	*999	*920	*843	*766	*691	*616	*542	*469	*397
6	.6325	254	185	116	047	*980	*913	*847	*782	*717
7	.5654	591	529	467	406	346	286	228	169	112
8	055	*999	*943	*889	*834	*781	*727	*675	*623	*572
9	.4521	471	421	372	324	276	229	182	136	090
5.0	045	000	*956	*912	*869	*826	*784	*742	*700	*660

$K_0(x)$

x	0	1	2	3	4	5	6	7	8	9
5.0	$10^{-2}\times$ 0.3691	651	611	572	533	494	456	419	382	345
1	308	272	237	202	167	132	098	065	031	*998
2	.2966	934	902	870	839	808	778	748	718	688
3	659	630	602	574	546	518	491	464	437	411
4	385	359	333	308	283	258	234	210	186	162
5	139	116	093	070	048	026	004	*982	*961	*939
6	.1918	898	877	857	837	817	798	778	759	740
7	721	703	684	666	648	630	613	595	578	561
8	544	528	511	495	479	463	447	432	416	401
9	386	371	356	342	327	313	299	285	271	258
6.0	244	231	217	204	191	179	166	153	141	129
1	117	105	093	081	070	058	047	035	024	013
2	0025	*9918	*9811	*9706	*9602	*9499	*9398	*9297	*9197	*9099
3	$10^{-3}\times$ 0.9001	8905	8810	8715	8622	8530	8438	8348	8259	8171
4	.8083	7997	7911	7827	7743	7660	7578	7497	7417	7338
5	.7259	182	105	029	*954	*880	*806	*734	*662	*591
6	.6520	451	382	314	246	180	114	048	*984	*920
7	.5857	795	733	672	611	551	492	434	376	318
8	262	206	150	095	041	*987	*934	*882	*830	*778
9	.4728	677	627	578	529	481	434	386	340	294
7.0	248	203	158	114	070	027	*984	*942	*900	*858
1	.3817	777	737	697	658	619	580	542	505	468
2	431	394	358	323	287	253	218	184	150	117
3	084	051	019	*987	*955	*924	*893	*862	*832	*802
4	.2772	742	713	685	656	628	600	573	545	518
5	492	465	439	413	388	363	338	313	288	264
6	240	216	193	170	147	124	102	079	057	036
7	014	*993	*972	*951	*930	*910	*890	*870	*850	*830
8	.1811	792	773	754	736	717	699	681	664	646
9	629	611	594	578	561	545	528	512	496	480
8.0	465	449	434	419	404	389	374	360	346	331
1	317	303	290	276	263	249	236	223	210	198
2	185	172	160	148	136	124	112	100	089	077
3	066	055	043	032	022	011	0002	*9897	*9793	*9690
4	$10^{-4}\times$ 0.9588	487	387	288	191	094	*998	*904	*810	*717
5	.8626	535	445	356	269	182	096	011	*926	*843
6	.7761	679	598	519	439	361	284	208	132	057
7	.6983	909	837	765	694	624	554	485	417	350
8	283	217	152	088	024	*961	*898	*836	*775	*714
9	.5654	595	536	478	420	364	307	252	197	142
9.0	088	035	*982	*930	*878	*827	*776	*726	*677	*628
1	.4579	531	484	437	390	344	299	254	209	165
2	121	078	036	*993	*951	*910	*869	*829	*789	*749
3	.3710	671	632	594	557	519	483	446	410	374
4	339	304	270	235	202	168	135	102	070	038
5	006	*974	*943	*912	*882	*852	*822	*793	*763	*734
6	.2706	678	650	622	595	567	541	514	488	462
7	436	411	385	360	336	311	287	263	240	216
8	193	170	148	125	103	081	059	038	017	*995
9	.1975	954	934	913	894	874	854	835	816	797
10.0	778	759	741	723	705	687	670	652	635	618

$K_1(x)$

x	0	1	2	3	4	5	6	7	8	9
5.0	$10^{-2}\times$ 0.4045	000	*956	*912	*869	*826	*784	*742	*700	*660
1	.3619	579	540	501	462	424	386	349	312	275
2	239	204	168	133	099	065	031	*998	*965	*982
3	.2900	868	836	805	774	744	714	684	655	625
4	597	568	540	512	485	457	430	404	377	351
5	326	300	275	250	225	201	177	153	130	106
6	083	060	038	016	*994	*972	*950	*929	*908	*887
7	.1866	846	826	806	786	767	748	729	710	691
8	673	654	636	619	601	584	566	549	532	516
9	499	483	467	451	435	419	404	389	374	359
6.0	344	329	315	301	286	273	259	245	232	218
1	205	192	179	166	154	141	129	116	104	092
2	081	069	057	046	034	023	012	0013	*9904	*9797
3	$10^{-3}\times$ 0.9691	586	483	380	279	178	079	*981	*884	*788
4	.8693	599	506	414	324	234	145	057	*970	*884
5	.7799	715	632	549	468	387	308	229	151	074
6	.6998	922	848	774	701	629	558	487	417	348
7	280	212	145	079	014	*949	*885	*822	*759	*697
8	.5636	576	516	456	398	340	282	226	170	114
9	059	005	*951	*898	*845	*793	*742	*691	*641	*591
7.0	.4542	493	445	397	350	304	257	212	167	122
1	078	034	*991	*948	*906	*864	*823	*782	*741	*701
2	.3662	623	584	545	508	470	433	396	360	324
3	288	253	219	184	150	116	083	050	018	*985
4	.2954	922	891	860	829	799	769	740	710	682
5	653	625	597	569	542	514	488	461	435	409
6	383	358	333	308	283	259	235	211	188	164
7	141	118	096	074	051	030	008	*987	*966	*945
8	.1924	903	883	863	843	824	804	785	766	747
9	729	710	692	674	656	639	621	604	587	570
8.0	554	537	521	505	489	473	457	442	427	411
1	396	382	367	352	338	324	310	296	282	269
2	255	242	229	216	203	190	177	165	153	140
3	128	116	105	093	081	070	058	047	036	025
4	014	0036	*9930	*9825	*9721	*9618	*9516	*9415	*9316	*9217
5	$10^{-4}\times$ 0.9120	023	*928	*833	*740	*648	*556	*466	*376	*288
6	.8200	113	028	*943	*859	*776	*694	*612	*532	*452
7	.7374	296	219	142	067	*992	*918	*845	*773	*702
8	.6631	561	492	423	355	288	222	156	091	027
9	.5964	901	838	777	716	656	596	537	479	421
9.0	364	307	251	196	141	087	033	*980	*928	*876
1	.4825	774	723	674	624	576	528	480	433	386
2	340	294	249	204	160	116	073	030	*988	*946
3	.3904	863	822	782	742	703	664	626	587	550
4	512	476	439	403	367	332	297	262	228	194
5	160	127	094	062	029	*998	*966	*935	*904	*874
6	.2843	814	784	755	726	697	669	641	613	586
7	559	532	505	479	453	427	402	377	352	327
8	302	278	254	231	207	184	161	139	116	094
9	072	050	029	008	*987	*966	*945	*925	*905	*885
10.0	.1865	845	826	807	788	769	751	732	714	696

E

THOMSON FUNCTIONS

Formulas

1. *Power series*

$$\text{ber } x = 1 - \frac{x^4}{2^4 \cdot 2\,!^2} + \frac{x^8}{2^8 \cdot 4\,!^2} - \frac{x^{12}}{2^{12} \cdot 6\,!^2} + - \cdots$$

$$\text{bei } x = \frac{x^2}{2^2 \cdot 1\,!^2} - \frac{x^6}{2^6 \cdot 3\,!^2} + \frac{x^{10}}{2^{10} \cdot 5\,!^2} - + \cdots$$

$$\text{ber}' x = - \frac{x^3}{2^3 \cdot 1! \cdot 2!} + \frac{x^7}{2^7 \cdot 3! \cdot 4!} - \frac{x^{11}}{2^{11} \cdot 5! \cdot 6!} + - \cdots$$

$$\text{bei}' x = \frac{x}{2 \cdot 0! \cdot 1!} - \frac{x^5}{2^5 \cdot 2! \cdot 3!} + \frac{x^9}{2^9 \cdot 4! \cdot 5!} - + \cdots$$

$$\text{ker } x = \frac{\pi}{4} \text{ bei } x - \ln \frac{\gamma\, x}{2} \cdot \text{ber } x -$$

$$- \frac{x^4}{2^4 \cdot 2\,!^2} \sum_1^2 \frac{1}{n} + \frac{x^8}{2^8 \cdot 4\,!^2} \sum_1^4 \frac{1}{n} - \frac{x^{12}}{2^{12} \cdot 6\,!^2} \sum_1^6 \frac{1}{n} + - \cdots$$

$$\text{kei } x = - \frac{\pi}{4} \text{ ber } x - \ln \frac{\gamma\, x}{2} \cdot \text{ bei } x +$$

$$+ \frac{x^2}{2^2 \cdot 1\,!^2} \sum_1^1 \frac{1}{n} - \frac{x^6}{2^6 \cdot 3\,!^2} \sum_1^3 \frac{1}{n} + \frac{x^{10}}{2^{10} \cdot 5\,!^2} \sum_1^5 \frac{1}{n} - + \cdots$$

$$\text{ker}' x = \frac{\pi}{4} \text{ bei}' x - \ln \frac{\gamma\, x}{2} \cdot \text{ber}' x - \frac{1}{x} \text{ ber } x -$$

$$- \frac{x^3}{2^3 \cdot 1! \cdot 2!} \sum_1^2 \frac{1}{n} + \frac{x^7}{2^7 \cdot 3! \cdot 4!} \sum_1^4 \frac{1}{n} - \frac{x^{11}}{2^{11} \cdot 5! \cdot 6!} \sum_1^6 \frac{1}{n} + - \cdots$$

$$\text{kei}' x = - \frac{\pi}{4} \text{ ber}' x - \ln \frac{\gamma\, x}{2} \cdot \text{ bei}' x - \frac{1}{x} \text{ bei } x +$$

$$+ \frac{x}{2 \cdot 0! \cdot 1!} \sum_1^1 \frac{1}{n} - \frac{x^5}{2^5 \cdot 2! \cdot 3!} \sum_1^3 \frac{1}{n} + \frac{x^9}{2^9 \cdot 4! \cdot 5!} \sum_1^5 \frac{1}{n} - + \cdots$$

2. *Asymptotic expansions*

See the general remark on asymptotic expansions on p. 39.

$$\text{ber } x = \frac{\exp(x/\sqrt{2})}{\sqrt{2\pi x}} \left[P_0(x) \cos\left(\frac{x}{\sqrt{2}} - \frac{\pi}{8}\right) + P_1(x) \sin\left(\frac{x}{\sqrt{2}} + \frac{\pi}{8}\right) + \right.$$

$$\left. + P_2(x) \sin\left(\frac{x}{\sqrt{2}} - \frac{\pi}{8}\right) - P_3(x) \cos\left(\frac{x}{\sqrt{2}} + \frac{\pi}{8}\right) \right]$$

$$\text{bei } x = \frac{\exp(x/\sqrt{2})}{\sqrt{2\pi x}} \left[P_0(x) \sin\left(\frac{x}{\sqrt{2}} - \frac{\pi}{8}\right) - P_1(x) \cos\left(\frac{x}{\sqrt{2}} + \frac{\pi}{8}\right) - \right.$$

$$\left. - P_2(x) \cos\left(\frac{x}{\sqrt{2}} - \frac{\pi}{8}\right) - P_3(x) \sin\left(\frac{x}{\sqrt{2}} + \frac{\pi}{8}\right) \right]$$

$$\text{ker } x = \sqrt{\frac{\pi}{2x}} \exp\left(-\frac{x}{\sqrt{2}}\right) \left[P_0(x) \cos\left(\frac{x}{\sqrt{2}} + \frac{\pi}{8}\right) + P_1(x) \sin\left(\frac{x}{\sqrt{2}} - \frac{\pi}{8}\right) - \right.$$

$$\left. - P_2(x) \sin\left(\frac{x}{\sqrt{2}} + \frac{\pi}{8}\right) + P_3(x) \cos\left(\frac{x}{\sqrt{2}} - \frac{\pi}{8}\right) \right]$$

$$\text{kei } x = - \sqrt{\frac{\pi}{2x}} \exp\left(-\frac{x}{\sqrt{2}}\right) \left[P_0(x) \sin\left(\frac{x}{\sqrt{2}} + \frac{\pi}{8}\right) - \right.$$

$$\left. - P_1(x) \cos\left(\frac{x}{\sqrt{2}} - \frac{\pi}{8}\right) + P_2(x) \cos\left(\frac{x}{\sqrt{2}} + \frac{\pi}{8}\right) + P_3(x) \sin\left(\frac{x}{\sqrt{2}} - \frac{\pi}{8}\right) \right]$$

with
$$P_0(x) \approx 1 - \frac{8!^2}{4!^3 \cdot 32^4 \cdot x^4} + \frac{16!^2}{8!^3 \cdot 32^8 \cdot x^8} - + \ldots$$

$$P_1(x) \approx \frac{2!^2}{1!^3 \cdot 32 \cdot x} - \frac{10!^2}{5!^3 \cdot 32^5 \cdot x^5} + - \ldots$$

$$P_2(x) \approx \frac{4!^2}{2!^3 \cdot 32^2 \cdot x^2} - \frac{12!^2}{6!^3 \cdot 32^6 \cdot x^6} + - \ldots$$

$$P_3(x) \approx \frac{6!^2}{3!^3 \cdot 32^3 \cdot x^3} - \frac{14!^2}{7!^3 \cdot 32^7 \cdot x^7} + - \ldots$$

$$\text{ber}' \, x = \frac{\exp(x/\sqrt{2})}{\sqrt{2\pi x}} \left[Q_0(x) \cos\left(\frac{x}{\sqrt{2}} + \frac{\pi}{8}\right) - Q_1(x) \cos\left(\frac{x}{\sqrt{2}} - \frac{\pi}{8}\right) - \right.$$

$$\left. - Q_2(x) \sin\left(\frac{x}{\sqrt{2}} + \frac{\pi}{8}\right) - Q_3(x) \sin\left(\frac{x}{\sqrt{2}} - \frac{\pi}{8}\right) \right]$$

$$\text{bei}' \, x = \frac{\exp(x/\sqrt{2})}{\sqrt{2\pi x}} \left[Q_0(x) \sin\left(\frac{x}{\sqrt{2}} + \frac{\pi}{8}\right) - Q_1(x) \sin\left(\frac{x}{\sqrt{2}} - \frac{\pi}{8}\right) + \right.$$

$$\left. + Q_2(x) \cos\left(\frac{x}{\sqrt{2}} + \frac{\pi}{8}\right) + Q_3(x) \cos\left(\frac{x}{\sqrt{2}} - \frac{\pi}{8}\right) \right]$$

$$\text{ker}' \, x = - \sqrt{\frac{\pi}{2x}} \exp\left(-\frac{x}{\sqrt{2}}\right) \left[Q_0(x) \cos\left(\frac{x}{\sqrt{2}} - \frac{\pi}{8}\right) + \right.$$

$$\left. + Q_1(x) \cos\left(\frac{x}{\sqrt{2}} + \frac{\pi}{8}\right) + Q_2(x) \sin\left(\frac{x}{\sqrt{2}} - \frac{\pi}{8}\right) - Q_3(x) \sin\left(\frac{x}{\sqrt{2}} + \frac{\pi}{8}\right) \right]$$

$$\text{kei}' \, x = \sqrt{\frac{\pi}{2x}} \exp\left(-\frac{x}{\sqrt{2}}\right) \left[Q_0(x) \sin\left(\frac{x}{\sqrt{2}} - \frac{\pi}{8}\right) + \right.$$

$$\left. + Q_1(x) \sin\left(\frac{x}{\sqrt{2}} + \frac{\pi}{8}\right) - Q_2(x) \cos\left(\frac{x}{\sqrt{2}} - \frac{\pi}{8}\right) + Q_3(x) \cos\left(\frac{x}{\sqrt{2}} + \frac{\pi}{8}\right) \right]$$

with
$$Q_0(x) \approx 1 + \frac{6! \cdot 10!}{3! \cdot 4! \cdot 5! \cdot 32^4 \cdot x^4} - \frac{14! \cdot 18!}{7! \cdot 8! \cdot 9! \cdot 32^8 \cdot x^8} + - \ldots$$

$$Q_1(x) \approx \frac{0! \cdot 4!}{0! \cdot 1! \cdot 2! \cdot 32 \cdot x} - \frac{8! \cdot 12!}{4! \cdot 5! \cdot 6! \cdot 32^5 \cdot x^5} + - \ldots$$

$$Q_2(x) \approx \frac{2! \cdot 6!}{1! \cdot 2! \cdot 3! \cdot 32^2 \cdot x^2} - \frac{10! \cdot 14!}{5! \cdot 6! \cdot 7! \cdot 32^6 \cdot x^6} + - \ldots$$

$$Q_3(x) \approx \frac{4! \cdot 8!}{2! \cdot 3! \cdot 4! \cdot 32^3 \cdot x^3} - \frac{12! \cdot 16!}{6! \cdot 7! \cdot 8! \cdot 32^7 \cdot x^7} + - \ldots$$

3. *Relations between Thomson functions and Bessel functions*

$$J_0 (x \sqrt{i}) = \text{ber } x - i \text{ bei } x$$

$$- \sqrt{i} J_1 (x \sqrt{i}) = \text{ber}' x - i \text{ bei}' x$$

$$K_0 (x \sqrt{i}) = \text{ker } x + i \text{ kei } x \qquad \sqrt{i} = \frac{1 + i}{\sqrt{2}} = e^{i\pi/4}$$

$$- \sqrt{i} K_1 (x \sqrt{i}) = \text{ker}' x + i \text{ kei}' x$$

4. *Derivatives*

The first derivatives of the Thomson functions ber x, bei x, ker x, kei x, are the functions ber$'$ x, bei$'$ x, ker$'$ x, kei$'$ x. They are another set of linearly independent functions, tabulated on pp. 72–75 and 80–83. The higher derivatives depend linearly on these eight functions:

$$\text{ber}'' x = - \text{bei } x - x^{-1} \text{ber}' x$$

$$\text{bei}'' x = \quad \text{ber } x - x^{-1} \text{bei}' x$$

$$\text{ker}'' x = - \text{kei } x - x^{-1} \text{ker}' x$$

$$\text{kei}'' x = \quad \text{ker } x - x^{-1} \text{kei}' x$$

Expressions for the third and higher derivatives may be obtained by differentiating these formulas and then eliminating on the right-hand side all derivatives of higher than the first order.

5. *Differential equations*

$$\frac{d^2 y}{dx^2} + \frac{1}{x} \frac{dy}{dx} - i n^2 y = 0:$$

$$y = A (\text{ber } nx + i \text{ bei } nx) + B (\text{ker } nx + i \text{ kei } nx)$$

$$\frac{d^2 y}{dx^2} + \frac{1}{x} \frac{dy}{dx} - \left(i n^2 + \frac{1}{x^2} \right) y = 0:$$

$$y = A (\text{ber}' nx + i \text{ bei}' nx) + B (\text{ker}' nx + i \text{ kei}' nx)$$

$$\left(\frac{d^2}{dx^2} + \frac{1}{x} \frac{d}{dx} \right)^2 y + n^4 y = 0:$$

$$y = A \text{ ber } nx + B \text{ bei } nx + C \text{ ker } nx + D \text{ kei } nx$$

$$\frac{d^2}{dx^2}\left(x^3 \frac{d^2 y}{dx^2}\right) + n^4\,x\,y = 0:$$

$$y = A\,x^{-1/2}\,\text{ber}'\,(2\,n\,x^{1/2}) + B\,x^{-1/2}\,\text{bei}'\,(2\,n\,x^{1/2})$$

$$+\,C\,x^{-1/2}\,\text{ker}'\,(2\,n\,x^{1/2}) + D\,x^{-1/2}\,\text{kei}'\,(2\,n\,x^{1/2})$$

6. Extreme values of the argument x

For very small arguments use the power series (1); for $x > 10$ use the asymptotic expansions (2).

7. Bibliography

A. G. WEBSTER: *Rep. 82nd Meeting*, Brit. Assoc. Advancement Sci., 1912, pp. 57–68.

ber x, bei x, ber'x, bei'x with 9 dec. for $x = 0.0\,(0.1)\,10.0$.

The values of bei'x for $x > 6.5$ are erroneous and have been corrected in the Rep. 86th Meeting, 1916, p. 122.

Mathematical Tables Project: *Table of the Bessel Functions $J_0\,(z)$ and $J_1\,(z)$ or Complex Arguments.* New York, 1943, pp. 182–201.

ber x, bei x, (bei'x − ber'x)/$\sqrt{2}$, (bei'x + ber'x)/$\sqrt{2}$ with 10 dec. for $x = 0.00\,(0.01)\,10.00$.

Author's notation:

$J_0\,(\rho\,e^{i\phi})$, real part and imaginary part, $\phi = 45°$, for ber ρ and − bei ρ, $J_1\,(\rho\,e^{i\phi})$, real part and imaginary part, $\phi = 45°$, for (bei'ρ − ber'ρ)/$\sqrt{2}$ and (bei'ρ + ber'ρ)/$\sqrt{2}$.

H. G. SAVIDGE: *Rep. 85th Meeting*, Brit. Assoc. Advancement Sci., 1915, pp. 36–38.

ker x, kei x, ker'x, kei'x with 6–7 dig. for $x = 0.0\,(0.1)\,10.00$.

F. TÖLKE: *Besselsche und Hankelsche Zylinderfunktionen nullter bis dritter Ordnung vom Argument $r\sqrt{i}$,* Stuttgart, 1936.

ber x, bei x, ber'x, bei'x
ker x, kei x, ker'x, kei'x } with 4 dig. for $x = 0.00\,(0.01)\,21.00$.

Author's notation:

$J_{01}(r)$, $J_{02}(r)$, $(J_{11}(r) - J_{12}(r))/\sqrt{2}$, $(J_{11}(r) + J_{12}(r))/\sqrt{2}$ for ber r, $-$ bei r, $-$ ber$'r$, bei$'r$;

$G_{01}(r)$, $G_{02}(r)$, $(G_{11}(r) - G_{12}(r))/\sqrt{2}$, $(G_{11}(r) + G_{12}(r))/\sqrt{2}$ for ker r, $-$ kei r, $-$ ker$'r$, kei$'r$.

THOMSON FUNCTIONS

ber x

x	0	1	2	3	4	5	6	7	8	9
0.0	1.0000	000	000	000	000	000	000	000	000	000
1	000	000	000	000	000	000	000	000	000	000
2	000	000	000	000	*999	*999	*999	*999	*999	*999
3	.9999	999	998	998	998	998	997	997	997	996
4	996	996	995	995	994	994	993	992	992	991
5	990	989	989	988	987	986	985	984	982	981
6	980	978	977	975	974	972	970	969	967	965
7	962	960	958	956	953	951	948	945	942	939
8	936	933	929	926	922	918	915	911	906	902
9	898	893	888	883	878	873	867	862	856	850
1.0	844	837	831	824	817	810	803	795	788	780
1	771	763	754	745	736	727	717	707	697	687
2	676	665	654	643	631	619	607	594	581	568
3	554	540	526	512	497	482	466	450	434	418
4	401	383	366	348	329	311	291	272	252	232
5	211	190	168	146	123	100	077	053	029	004
6	.8979	953	927	900	873	846	817	789	760	730
7	700	669	638	606	573	541	507	473	438	403
8	367	331	294	256	218	179	140	099	059	017
9	.7975	933	889	845	800	755	709	662	615	566
2.0	517	468	417	366	314	262	208	154	099	043
1	.6987	930	871	813	753	692	631	569	506	442
2	377	311	245	177	109	040	*970	*899	*827	*754
3	.5680	606	530	454	376	298	218	138	056	*974
4	.4890	806	721	634	547	458	369	278	186	094
5	000	*905	*809	*712	*614	*514	*414	*312	*210	*106
6	.3001	2895	2788	2679	2570	2459	2347	2234	2119	2004
7	.1887	1769	1650	1529	1408	1285	1161	1035	0908	0780
8	+.0651	0521	0389	0256	0121	*0015	*0152	*0290	*0430	*0571
9	−.0714	0857	1003	1149	1297	1446	1597	1749	1903	2058
3.0	−.2214	2371	2531	2691	2853	3017	3181	3348	3515	3685
1	−.3855	4027	4201	4376	4553	4731	4910	5091	5274	5458
2	−.5644	5831	6020	6210	6401	6595	6789	6986	7184	7383
3	−.7584	7787	7991	8196	8404	8613	8823	9035	9248	9464
4	−.9680	9899	*0119	*034	*056	*079	*101	*124	*147	*170
5	−1.194	217	241	264	288	312	337	361	386	410
6	435	460	486	511	537	562	588	614	640	667
7	693	720	747	774	801	828	856	883	911	939
8	967	996	*024	*053	*082	*111	*140	*169	*198	*228
9	−2.258	287	318	348	378	409	439	470	501	532
4.0	563	595	626	658	690	722	754	786	819	852
1	884	917	950	983	*017	*050	*084	*117	*151	*185
2	−3.219	254	288	323	357	392	427	462	497	533
3	568	603	639	675	711	747	783	819	855	892
4	928	965	*002	*039	*075	*113	*150	*187	*224	*262
5	−4.299	337	374	412	450	488	526	564	602	640
6	678	717	755	793	832	870	909	948	986	*025
7	−5.064	103	142	180	219	258	297	336	375	414
8	453	492	531	570	609	648	687	726	765	804
9	843	882	921	960	998	*037	*076	*114	*153	*192
5.0	−6.230	269	307	345	383	421	459	497	535	573

bei x

x	0	1	2	3	4	5	6	7	8	9
0.0	.00000	0000	0010	0022	0040	0062	0090	0122	0160	0202
1	0250	0302	0360	0422	0490	0562	0640	0722	0810	0902
2	1000	1102	1210	1322	1440	1562	1690	1822	1960	2102
3	2250	2402	2560	2722	2890	3062	3240	3422	3610	3802
4	4000	4202	4410	4622	4840	5062	5290	5522	5759	6002
5	6249	6502	6759	7022	7289	7561	7839	8121	8408	8701
6	8998	9300	9608	9920	*024	*056	*089	*122	*156	*190
7	.1224	260	295	332	368	405	443	481	520	559
8	599	639	680	721	762	805	847	890	934	978
9	.2023	068	113	159	206	253	301	349	397	446
1.0	496	546	596	647	699	750	803	856	909	963
1	.3017	072	127	183	239	296	353	411	469	528
2	587	647	707	767	828	890	952	*014	*077	*140
3	.4204	268	333	398	464	530	597	664	731	799
4	867	936	*005	*075	*145	*216	*287	*358	*430	*503
5	.5576	649	723	797	871	946	*022	*097	*174	*250
6	.6327	405	483	561	640	719	798	878	959	*039
7	.7120	202	284	366	449	532	615	699	783	868
8	953	*038	*124	*210	*296	*383	*470	*557	*645	*733
9	.8821	910	999	*088	*178	*268	*358	*449	*540	*631
2.0	.9723	815	907	999	*092	*185	*278	*372	*466	*560
1	1.065	075	084	094	103	113	122	132	142	151
2	161	171	180	190	200	210	219	229	239	249
3	259	268	278	288	298	308	318	328	338	348
4	357	367	377	387	397	407	417	427	437	447
5	457	467	477	487	497	507	517	527	537	547
6	557	567	577	587	597	606	616	626	636	646
7	656	666	675	685	695	705	714	724	734	743
8	753	762	772	781	791	800	810	819	829	838
9	847	856	866	875	884	893	902	911	920	929
3.0	938	946	955	964	972	981	989	998	*006	*015
1	2.023	031	039	047	055	063	071	079	086	094
2	102	109	116	124	131	138	145	152	159	166
3	172	179	185	192	198	204	210	216	222	228
4	233	239	244	250	255	260	265	270	274	279
5	283	288	292	296	300	303	307	310	314	317
6	320	323	325	328	330	333	335	337	338	340
7	341	343	344	344	345	346	346	346	346	346
8	345	345	344	343	342	340	339	337	335	333
9	330	327	324	321	318	314	310	306	302	297
4.0	293	288	282	277	271	265	259	252	245	238
1	231	223	215	207	199	190	181	172	162	152
2	142	132	121	110	098	087	075	062	050	037
3	024	010	*996	*982	*967	*952	*937	*921	*906	*889
4	1.873	856	838	820	802	784	765	746	726	706
5	686	665	644	623	601	579	556	533	509	485
6	461	436	411	386	360	333	306	279	251	223
7	195	166	136	106	076	045	014	*9818	*9496	*9168
8	.8837	8500	8159	7812	7461	7105	6745	6379	6008	5632
9	.5251	4866	4475	4079	3677	3271	2859	2443	2020	1593
5.0	.1160	0722	0279	*0170	*0624	*1084	*1550	*2021	*2497	*2979

ber x

x	0	1	2	3	4	5	6	7	8	9
5.0	− 10 × 0.6230	269	307	345	383	421	459	497	535	573
1	611	648	686	723	760	797	834	871	908	944
2	980	*017	*053	*088	*124	*160	*195	*230	*265	*300
3	.7334	369	403	437	470	504	537	570	603	635
4	667	699	731	762	793	824	855	885	915	944
5	974	*002	*031	*059	*087	*115	*142	*169	*195	*221
6	.8247	272	297	321	345	368	392	414	436	458
7	479	500	520	540	560	578	597	614	632	648
8	664	680	695	709	723	737	749	761	773	784
9	794	803	812	820	828	835	841	846	851	855
6.0	858	861	863	864	864	864	862	860	857	854
1	849	844	838	830	823	814	804	793	782	769
2	756	742	726	710	693	675	656	636	614	592
3	569	544	519	493	465	436	407	376	344	311
4	276	241	204	166	127	087	045	003	*959	*913
5	.7867	819	770	720	668	615	560	504	447	389
6	329	267	204	140	075	007	*939	*869	*797	*724
7	.6649	573	495	416	335	252	168	083	*995	*906
8	.5816	5723	5629	5533	5436	5337	5236	5133	5029	4923
9	.4815	4705	4593	4480	4364	4247	4128	4007	3884	3760
7.0	.3633	3504	3374	3241	3107	2970	2832	2691	2548	2404
1	.2257	2108	1957	1805	1649	1492	1333	1171	1008	0842
2	.0674	0503	0331	0156	*0021	*0200	*0382	*0565	*0752	*0940
3	+ 10 × 0.1131	1324	1519	1717	1917	2120	2325	2533	2742	2955
4	.3169	3387	3606	3829	4053	4281	4510	4743	4978	5215
5	.5455	5698	5943	6191	6441	6694	6950	7208	7469	7733
6	.7999	8269	8540	8815	9092	9372	9655	9941	*0229	*052
7	+ 10² × 0.1081	111	141	171	202	233	264	295	327	359
8	391	423	456	489	523	556	590	625	659	694
9	729	765	801	837	873	910	947	984	*021	*059
8.0	.2097	136	175	214	253	293	333	373	414	454
1	496	537	579	621	664	706	749	793	836	880
2	925	969	*014	*059	*105	*150	*197	*243	*290	*337
3	.3384	432	480	528	576	625	674	724	773	823
4	874	924	975	*027	*078	*130	*182	*235	*287	*340
5	.4394	4447	4501	4555	4610	4664	4719	4775	4830	4886
6	.4942	4999	5055	5112	5170	5227	5285	5343	5401	5460
7	.5519	5578	5637	5697	5757	5817	5877	5938	5999	6060
8	.6121	6183	6244	6306	6369	6431	6494	6557	6620	6683
9	.6747	6811	6875	6939	7003	7068	7133	7198	7263	7328
9.0	.7394	7459	7525	7591	7657	7724	7790	7857	7924	7991
1	.8058	8125	8192	8260	8327	8395	8463	8531	8599	8667
2	.8735	8803	8872	8940	9009	9077	9146	9215	9283	9352
3	.9421	9490	9559	9627	9696	9765	9834	9903	9972	*0041
4	+ 10³ × 0.1011	018	025	032	038	045	052	059	066	073
5	080	086	093	100	107	113	120	127	134	140
6	147	154	160	167	173	180	187	193	200	206
7	213	219	225	232	238	244	251	257	263	269
8	275	281	287	294	299	305	311	317	323	329
9	334	340	346	351	357	362	367	373	378	383
10.0	388	393	399	403	408	413	418	423	427	432

bei x

x	0	1	2	3	4	5	6	7	8	9
5.0	+ 0.1160	0722	0279	*0170	*0624	*1084	*1550	*2021	*2497	*2979
1	− 0.3467	3960	4459	4964	5474	5990	6512	7040	7574	8113
2	− 0.8658	9210	9767	*0330	*090	*147	*206	*264	*324	*384
3	− 1.444	505	567	630	693	757	821	886	951	*018
4	− 2.085	152	220	289	358	429	499	571	643	716
5	− 2.789	863	938	*013	*089	*166	*243	*321	*400	*480
6	− 3.560	641	722	804	887	971	*055	*140	*225	*312
7	− 4.399	486	575	664	753	844	935	*027	*120	*213
8	− 5.307	402	497	593	690	787	886	984	*084	*184
9	− 6.285	387	490	593	697	801	907	*013	*119	*227
6.0	− 7.335	444	553	663	774	886	998	*111	*225	*339
1	− 8.454	570	687	804	922	*041	*160	*280	*400	*522
2	− 9.644	766	890	*014	*14	*26	*39	*52	*64	*77
3	− 10 × 1.090	103	116	129	142	155	169	182	195	209
4	222	236	249	263	277	291	305	319	333	347
5	361	375	389	403	418	432	446	461	475	490
6	505	519	534	549	564	579	594	609	624	639
7	654	669	684	699	715	730	745	761	776	792
8	807	823	839	854	870	886	901	917	933	949
9	964	980	996	*012	*028	*044	*060	*076	*092	*108
7.0	2.124	140	156	172	188	204	220	236	253	269
1	285	301	317	333	349	365	381	397	414	430
2	446	462	478	494	510	526	542	557	573	589
3	605	621	636	652	668	683	699	715	730	745
4	761	776	792	807	822	837	852	867	882	897
5	912	926	941	955	970	984	999	*013	*027	*041
6	3.055	069	082	096	110	123	136	149	162	175
7	188	201	214	226	238	250	262	274	286	298
8	309	320	332	343	353	364	375	385	395	405
9	415	424	434	443	452	461	469	478	486	494
8.0	502	509	517	524	531	537	544	550	556	561
1	567	572	577	581	586	590	594	597	600	603
2	606	608	611	612	614	615	616	616	617	616
3	616	615	614	612	611	608	606	603	600	596
4	592	588	583	578	572	566	560	553	545	538
5	530	521	512	503	493	483	472	461	449	437
6	425	412	398	384	369	354	339	323	306	289
7	271	253	235	215	196	175	154	133	111	088
8	065	041	017	*992	*967	*940	*914	*886	*858	*830
9	2.800	770	740	709	677	644	611	577	542	507
9.0	471	435	397	359	320	281	241	200	158	116
1	072	028	*984	*938	*892	*845	*797	*748	*699	*649
2	1.598	546	493	440	385	330	274	217	159	101
3	041	*981	*920	*857	*794	*730	*666	*600	*533	*465
4	0.397	327	257	186	113	040	*034	*11	*19	*26
5	+ 10 × 0.341	420	500	582	664	747	831	917	*003	*090
6	1.179	268	359	450	543	637	732	827	924	*023
7	2.122	222	324	426	530	635	740	848	956	*065
8	3.176	287	400	514	630	746	864	982	*102	*224
9	4.346	470	594	720	848	976	*106	*237	*369	*502
10.0	5.637	773	910	*049	*188	*329	*472	*615	*760	*906

THOMSON FUNCTIONS

ber′ x

x	0	1	2	3	4	5	6	7	8	9
0.0	− 10⁻⁴ × 0.0000	0006	0050	0169	0400	0781	1350	2144	3200	4556
1	− 10⁻³ × 0.06250	08319	1080	1373	1715	2109	2560	3071	3645	4287
2	.5000	5788	6655	7604	8640	9766	*098	*230	*372	*524
3	− 10⁻² × 0.1687	1862	2048	2246	2456	2680	2916	3166	3429	3707
4	.4000	4307	4630	4969	5324	5695	6083	6489	6912	7353
5	.7812	8290	8787	9304	9841	*040	*098	*157	*219	*283
6	− 10⁻¹ × 0.1350	1418	1489	1563	1638	1716	1797	1879	1965	2053
7	.2143	2236	2332	2431	2532	2636	2743	2852	2965	3080
8	.3199	3320	3445	3572	3703	3837	3973	4114	4257	4404
9	.4554	4707	4864	5024	5188	5355	5526	5700	5878	6060
1.0	.6245	6434	6626	6823	7023	7228	7436	7648	7864	8084
1	.8308	8536	8768	9005	9246	9491	9740	9994	*025	*051
2	− 10⁰ × 0.1078	105	133	161	189	218	248	277	308	338
3	370	401	434	466	500	533	568	602	637	673
4	709	746	783	821	859	898	937	977	*018	*059
5	.2100	142	185	228	272	316	361	406	452	498
6	545	593	641	690	740	790	840	891	943	995
7	.3048	102	156	211	266	322	379	436	494	553
8	612	672	732	793	855	917	980	*044	*108	*173
9	.4238	305	372	439	507	576	646	716	787	858
2.0	931	*004	*077	*151	*226	*302	*378	*455	*533	*612
1	.5691	770	851	932	*014	*097	*180	*264	*348	*434
2	.6520	607	694	783	872	961	*052	*143	*234	*327
3	.7420	514	609	704	800	897	995	*093	*192	*292
4	.8392	493	595	698	801	905	*010	*115	*221	*328
5	.9436	544	653	763	873	985	*10	*21	*32	*44
6	− 10 × 0.1055	067	078	090	102	114	125	137	149	162
7	174	186	198	211	223	236	248	261	274	286
8	299	312	325	338	351	365	378	391	404	418
9	431	445	459	472	486	500	514	528	542	556
3.0	570	584	598	613	627	641	656	670	685	699
1	714	729	744	758	773	788	803	818	833	848
2	864	879	894	909	925	940	956	971	987	*002
3	.2018	033	049	065	080	096	112	128	144	160
4	175	191	207	223	239	256	272	288	304	320
5	336	352	368	385	401	417	433	450	466	482
6	498	515	531	547	563	580	596	612	628	645
7	661	677	693	709	726	742	758	774	790	806
8	822	838	854	870	886	902	918	934	949	965
9	981	996	*012	*028	*043	*058	*074	*089	*104	*120
4.0	.3135	150	165	180	194	209	224	239	253	267
1	282	296	310	324	338	352	366	380	393	407
2	420	433	446	459	472	485	497	510	522	534
3	547	558	570	582	593	605	616	627	638	648
4	659	669	679	689	699	709	718	727	736	745
5	754	762	770	778	786	794	801	808	815	822
6	828	834	840	846	851	856	861	866	870	874
7	878	882	885	888	891	893	895	897	899	900
8	901	901	901	901	901	900	899	898	896	894
9	891	888	885	881	877	873	868	863	858	852
5.0	845	839	831	824	816	808	799	789	780	770

bei′x

x	0	1	2	3	4	5	6	7	8	9
0.0	.00000	0500	1000	1500	2000	2500	3000	3500	4000	4500
1	5000	5500	6000	6500	7000	7500	8000	8500	9000	9500
2	.1000	050	100	150	200	250	300	350	400	450
3	500	550	600	650	700	750	800	850	900	950
4	.2000	050	100	150	200	250	299	349	399	449
5	499	549	599	649	699	749	799	848	898	948
6	998	*048	*098	*147	*197	*247	*297	*346	*396	*446
7	.3496	545	595	645	694	744	793	843	892	942
8	991	*041	*090	*140	*189	*238	*288	*337	*386	*435
9	.4485	534	583	632	681	730	779	828	876	925
1.0	974	*023	*071	*120	*168	*217	*265	*313	*362	*410
1	.5458	506	554	602	650	698	745	793	840	888
2	935	982	*030	*077	*124	*171	*217	*264	*311	*357
3	.6403	450	496	542	588	633	679	724	770	815
4	860	905	950	994	*039	*083	*127	*171	*215	*259
5	.7303	346	389	432	475	517	560	602	644	686
6	727	769	810	851	892	932	972	*012	*052	*092
7	.8131	170	209	247	286	324	361	399	436	473
8	509	546	581	617	652	687	722	756	790	824
9	857	890	923	955	987	*019	*050	*080	*111	*141
2.0	.9170	199	228	256	284	311	338	365	391	417
1	442	466	491	514	538	560	583	604	625	646
2	666	686	705	723	741	758	775	791	807	822
3	836	850	863	875	887	898	909	919	928	936
4	944	951	958	964	969	973	976	979	981	982
5	983	982	981	979	977	973	969	963	957	950
6	943	934	924	914	903	890	877	863	848	832
7	815	797	778	758	737	715	692	668	643	617
8	590	561	532	502	470	437	403	368	332	295
9	257	217	176	134	091	046	001	*953	*905	*856
3.0	.8805	753	699	644	588	531	472	412	350	287
1	223	157	090	021	*951	*880	*807	*732	*656	*578
2	.7499	419	336	253	167	080	*992	*902	*810	*716
3	.6621	525	426	326	224	121	016	*909	*800	*689
4	.5577	463	347	229	110	*988	*865	*740	*613	*484
5	.4353	4220	4085	3949	3810	3670	3527	3382	3236	3087
6	.2937	2784	2629	2472	2313	2152	1989	1824	1656	1487
7	+.1315	1141	0965	0786	0606	0423	0238	0050	*0139	*0331
8	−.0525	0722	0921	1122	1325	1531	1740	1950	2163	2379
9	−.2597	2817	3040	3265	3493	3723	3955	4191	4428	4669
4.0	−.4911	5157	5405	5655	5908	6164	6422	6683	6947	7213
1	−.7482	7753	8027	8304	8584	8866	9151	9439	9729	*0023
2	−1.032	062	092	122	153	184	215	247	279	311
3	343	376	409	442	476	510	544	578	613	648
4	683	719	755	791	827	864	901	939	976	*014
5	−2.053	091	130	169	209	249	289	329	370	411
6	452	494	536	578	620	663	706	750	793	837
7	882	926	971	*017	*062	*108	*154	*201	*248	*295
8	−3.342	390	438	486	535	584	633	683	732	783
9	833	884	935	986	*038	*090	*142	*195	*248	*301
5.0	−4.354	408	462	516	571	626	681	736	792	848

ber′ x

x	0	1	2	3	4	5	6	7	8	9
5.0	− 10 × 0.3845	839	831	824	816	808	799	789	780	770
1	759	748	736	724	712	699	686	672	657	642
2	627	611	595	578	560	542	524	505	485	465
3	445	423	402	379	356	333	309	284	259	233
4	206	179	152	123	094	065	034	004	*972	*940
5	.2907	874	839	804	769	733	696	658	620	581
6	541	500	459	417	375	331	287	242	196	150
7	102	054	005	*956	*905	*854	*802	*749	*695	*641
8	.1586	529	472	414	356	296	235	174	112	048
9	.0984	919	854	787	719	650	581	510	439	366
6.0	293	219	143	067	*010	*088	*167	*248	*329	*411
1	+ 10 × 0.0494	0579	0664	0750	0837	0926	1015	1106	1197	1290
2	.1384	1478	1574	1671	1769	1868	1968	2070	2172	2276
3	.2380	2486	2593	2701	2810	2921	3032	3145	3259	3374
4	.3490	3607	3726	3846	3966	4089	4212	4336	4462	4589
5	.4717	4847	4977	5109	5242	5377	5512	5649	5787	5927
6	.6067	6209	6353	6497	6643	6790	6938	7088	7239	7391
7	.7544	7699	7855	8012	8171	8331	8492	8655	8819	8984
8	.9151	9319	9488	9659	9831	*0004	*018	*035	*053	*071
9	+ 10² × 0.1089	107	125	144	162	181	200	219	238	257
7.0	276	296	316	335	355	375	395	416	436	457
1	477	498	519	540	562	583	604	626	648	670
2	692	714	736	759	781	804	827	850	873	896
3	919	943	967	990	*014	*038	*062	*086	*111	*135
4	.2160	185	210	235	260	285	310	336	361	387
5	413	439	465	491	518	544	570	597	624	651
6	678	705	732	759	787	814	842	869	897	925
7	953	981	*009	*038	*066	*095	*123	*152	*181	*209
8	.3238	267	296	325	355	384	413	443	472	502
9	531	561	591	621	651	681	711	741	771	801
8.0	831	861	892	922	952	983	*013	*044	*074	*105
1	.4135	166	196	227	258	288	319	350	380	411
2	442	472	503	533	564	595	625	656	686	717
3	747	778	808	838	869	899	929	959	989	*019
4	.5049	079	109	139	168	198	227	257	286	315
5	344	373	402	431	459	488	516	544	572	600
6	628	656	683	710	738	765	791	818	844	871
7	897	923	948	973	999	*024	*048	*073	*097	*121
8	.6145	169	192	215	238	260	282	304	326	347
9	368	389	409	429	449	468	487	506	524	542
9.0	560	577	594	611	627	642	658	673	687	701
1	714	728	740	753	764	776	786	797	806	816
2	825	833	841	848	855	861	866	871	876	880
3	883	886	888	889	890	891	890	889	887	885
4	882	878	874	869	863	857	849	841	833	823
5	813	802	790	778	765	750	736	720	703	686
6	667	648	628	607	585	563	539	515	489	463
7	435	407	378	347	316	284	251	216	181	144
8	107	068	029	*988	*946	*903	*859	*814	*768	*721
9	.5672	622	571	519	466	411	355	298	240	180
10.0	120	057	*994	*929	*863	*796	*727	*657	*585	*513

bei′ x

x	0	1	2	3	4	5	6	7	8	9
5.0	− 10 × 0.4354	408	462	516	571	626	681	736	792	848
1	905	961	*018	*075	*133	*191	*249	*307	*366	*424
2	.5484	543	603	662	723	783	844	905	966	*028
3	.6089	151	214	276	339	402	465	528	592	656
4	720	784	849	914	979	*044	*109	*175	*241	*307
5	.7373	439	506	573	640	707	774	842	909	977
6	.8045	114	182	250	319	388	457	526	595	664
7	734	803	873	942	*012	*082	*152	*222	*293	*363
8	.9433	504	574	645	715	786	857	927	998	*069
9	− 10² × 0.1014	021	028	035	042	049	056	063	071	078
6.0	085	092	099	106	113	120	127	134	141	148
1	155	162	169	176	182	189	196	203	210	217
2	223	230	237	244	250	257	264	270	277	284
3	290	297	303	310	316	322	329	335	341	347
4	354	360	366	372	378	384	390	396	401	407
5	413	419	424	430	435	441	446	451	457	462
6	467	472	477	482	487	492	496	501	506	510
7	515	519	523	527	532	536	540	543	547	551
8	554	558	561	565	568	571	574	577	579	582
9	585	587	590	592	594	596	598	600	601	603
7.0	604	605	607	608	608	609	610	610	611	611
1	611	611	611	610	610	609	608	607	606	605
2	603	602	600	598	596	593	591	588	585	582
3	579	576	572	568	565	560	556	552	547	542
4	537	531	526	520	514	508	501	495	488	481
5	474	466	458	450	442	434	425	416	407	397
6	388	378	367	357	346	335	324	312	301	289
7	276	264	251	238	224	210	196	182	167	152
8	137	122	106	090	073	057	040	022	004	*9864
9	− 10 × 0.9681	9494	9304	9110	8913	8713	8510	8302	8092	7878
8.0	.7660	7439	7215	6986	6754	6519	6280	6037	5790	5540
1	.5285	5027	4766	4500	4230	3957	3679	3398	3113	2823
2	.2530	2232	1930	1624	1315	1000	0682	0359	0033	*0299
3	+ 10 × 0.0634	0974	1318	1667	2020	2377	2739	3105	3476	3852
4	.4232	4616	5006	5400	5798	6202	6610	7022	7440	7862
5	.8290	8722	9158	9600	*0047	*050	*096	*142	*188	*236
6	+ 10² × 0.1283	331	380	429	479	529	580	631	683	735
7	788	842	896	950	*005	*061	*117	*173	*231	*288
8	.2347	405	465	525	585	646	708	770	833	896
9	960	*024	*089	*155	*221	*288	*355	*423	*491	*560
9.0	.3630	700	771	842	914	987	*060	*134	*208	*283
1	.4358	434	511	588	666	745	824	903	984	*065
2	.5146	5228	5311	5394	5478	5562	5647	5733	5819	5906
3	.5994	6082	6170	6260	6349	6440	6531	6623	6715	6808
4	.6901	6995	7090	7185	7281	7377	7474	7572	7670	7769
5	.7868	7968	8069	8170	8272	8374	8477	8580	8684	8789
6	.8894	9000	9106	9213	9320	9428	9537	9646	9755	9866
7	.9976	*0089	*020	*031	*042	*054	*065	*077	*088	*100
8	+ 10³ × 0.1111	123	135	146	158	170	182	194	206	218
9	230	242	254	266	279	291	303	316	328	341
10.0	353	366	378	391	404	416	429	442	455	467

ker x

x	0	1	2	3	4	5	6	7	8	9
0.0	∞	4.721	4.028	3.623	3.335	3.112	2.930	2.776	2.643	2.525
1	2.420	326	239	159	086	017	*954	*894	*837	*784
2	1.733	685	639	596	554	514	476	439	404	370
3	337	306	275	245	217	189	162	136	111	086
4	063	039	0169	*9949	*9735	*9527	*9321	*9125	*8932	*8743
5	0.8559	8379	8204	8032	7864	7700	7540	7383	7229	7078
6	.6931	787	646	508	372	239	109	*982	*857	*734
7	.5614	496	380	267	155	046	*939	*833	*730	*628
8	.4529	431	335	241	148	057	*967	*880	*793	*708
9	.3625	543	463	384	306	230	155	081	008	*937
1.0	.2867	798	730	664	598	534	471	409	348	288
1	228	170	113	057	002	*948	*894	*842	*790	*739
2	.1689	640	592	545	498	452	407	363	319	277
3	235	193	153	113	073	035	*9967	*9594	*9227	*8867
4	$10^{-1} \times$ 0.8513	8165	7823	7486	7156	6832	6513	6200	5892	5590
5	.5293	5002	4716	4434	4158	3887	3621	3359	3102	2850
6	.2603	2360	2122	1888	1658	1433	1212	0995	0782	0574
7	.0369	0168	*0028	*0221	*0411	*0596	*0778	*0956	*1131	*1302
8	$- 10^{-1} \times$ 0.1470	1634	1795	1952	2107	2258	2406	2550	2692	2831
9	.2966	3099	3229	3355	3479	3601	3719	3835	3948	4059
2.0	.4166	272	375	475	573	668	761	852	941	*027
1	.5111	192	272	349	425	498	569	638	705	771
2	834	895	955	*012	*068	*122	*175	*225	*274	*321
3	.6367	411	453	494	533	571	607	642	675	707
4	737	766	794	820	845	869	891	913	933	951
5	969	985	*000	*014	*027	*039	*050	*060	*068	*076
6	.7083	088	093	097	099	101	102	102	102	100
7	097	094	090	085	079	073	066	058	050	040
8	030	019	007	*995	*983	*969	*955	*941	*926	*910
9	.6894	877	860	842	823	805	785	765	745	724
3.0	703	681	659	637	614	590	567	542	518	493
1	468	442	416	390	364	337	310	282	255	227
2	198	170	141	112	083	054	024	*994	*964	*934
3	.5903	873	842	811	780	748	717	685	654	622
4	590	558	525	493	460	428	395	363	330	297
5	264	231	198	165	132	098	065	032	*998	*965
6	.4932	898	865	831	798	764	731	697	664	631
7	597	564	530	497	464	430	397	364	331	298
8	265	232	199	166	133	100	067	035	002	*970
9	.3937	905	873	841	808	776	745	713	681	649
4.0	618	586	555	524	493	462	431	400	370	339
1	308	278	248	218	188	158	128	099	069	040
2	011	*982	*953	*924	*895	*867	*838	*810	*782	*754
3	.2726	698	671	644	616	589	562	535	509	482
4	456	429	403	377	352	326	300	275	250	225
5	200	175	151	126	102	078	054	030	006	*983
6	.1960	936	913	890	868	845	823	800	778	756
7	734	713	691	670	649	628	607	586	566	545
8	525	505	485	465	445	426	406	387	368	349
9	330	312	293	275	257	239	221	203	186	168
5.0	151	134	117	100	084	067	051	034	018	002

kei x

x	0	1	2	3	4	5	6	7	8	9
0.0	− 0.7854	853	849	844	837	828	819	808	796	783
1	769	753	737	721	703	684	665	645	625	603
2	581	559	535	512	487	463	437	411	385	358
3	331	303	275	247	218	189	159	129	099	069
4	038	007	*976	*944	*912	*880	*847	*815	*782	*749
5	− 0.6716	682	649	615	581	547	513	478	444	409
6	374	340	305	270	234	199	164	128	093	057
7	022	*986	*950	*915	*879	*843	*807	*771	*735	*700
8	− 0.5664	628	592	556	520	484	448	412	377	341
9	305	269	234	198	162	127	091	056	021	*985
1.0	− 0.4950	915	880	845	810	775	740	705	670	636
1	601	567	533	498	464	430	396	362	329	295
2	262	228	195	162	129	096	063	030	*998	*965
3	− 0.3933	901	869	837	805	773	742	710	679	648
4	617	586	555	524	494	464	433	403	373	344
5	314	284	255	226	197	168	139	111	082	054
6	026	*998	*970	*942	*914	*887	*860	*833	*806	*779
7	− 0.2752	726	699	673	647	621	596	570	545	519
8	494	469	444	420	395	371	347	323	299	275
9	251	228	205	182	159	136	113	091	068	046
2.0	024	002	*980	*959	*937	*916	*895	*874	*853	*832
1	− 0.1812	791	771	751	731	711	692	672	653	633
2	614	595	577	558	539	521	503	485	467	449
3	431	414	396	379	362	345	328	312	295	279
4	262	246	230	214	199	183	168	152	137	122
5	107	092	077	063	048	034	020	0059	*9919	*9781
6	− $10^{-1} \times$ 0.9644	509	374	241	109	*978	*849	*720	*593	*467
7	.8342	219	096	*975	*854	*735	*618	*501	*385	*270
8	.7157	045	*934	*823	*714	*606	*500	*394	*289	*185
9	.6083	*981	*880	*781	*682	*585	*488	*393	*298	*205
3.0	.5112	021	*930	*840	*752	*664	*577	*491	*407	*323
1	.4240	157	076	*996	*916	*838	*760	*683	*607	*532
2	.3458	385	312	241	170	100	031	*962	*895	*828
3	.2762	697	632	569	506	444	382	322	262	203
4	145	087	030	*974	*918	*864	*810	*756	*704	*652
5	.1600	550	500	450	402	354	306	260	213	168
6	123	079	035	*9922	*9498	*9080	*8668	*8261	*7861	*7466
7	− $10^{-2} \times$ 0.7077	6693	6315	5943	5576	5214	4858	4507	4162	3822
8	.3487	3157	2832	2512	2197	1888	1583	1282	0987	0697
9	.0411	0130	*0147	*0419	*0686	*0949	*1208	*1462	*1712	*1957
4.0	+ $10^{-2} \times$ 0.2198	2435	2668	2897	3122	3342	3559	3771	3980	4185
1	.4386	4583	4776	4966	5152	5335	5513	5689	5860	6029
2	.6194	355	513	668	819	968	*113	*254	*393	*529
3	.7661	791	917	*041	*161	*279	*394	*506	*615	*722
4	.8826	927	*025	*121	*214	*305	*393	*479	*562	*643
5	.9721	797	871	942	*011	*08	*14	*20	*26	*32
6	1.038	043	048	053	058	063	067	071	075	079
7	083	086	090	093	096	098	101	103	106	108
8	110	112	113	115	116	117	118	119	120	120
9	121	121	122	122	122	121	121	121	120	120
5.0	119	118	117	116	115	113	112	110	109	107

F

ker x

x	0	1	2	3	4	5	6	7	8	9
5.0	$- 10^{-1}\times$ 0.1151	1134	1117	1100	1084	1067	1051	1034	1018	10023
1	$- 10^{-2}\times$ 0.9865	9708	9552	9398	9246	9095	8945	8796	8649	8503
2	.8359	8216	8074	7934	7795	7658	7521	7386	7253	7120
3	.6989	860	731	604	478	353	230	108	*987	*867
4	.5749	632	516	401	288	176	065	*955	*846	*739
5	.4632	527	423	320	218	118	018	*920	*823	*727
6	.3632	538	445	353	262	173	084	*997	*910	*825
7	.2740	657	575	493	413	334	255	178	101	026
8	.1952	878	805	734	663	593	525	457	390	323
9	258	194	130	068	006	*945	*885	*826	*767	*710
6.0	.0653	597	542	488	434	382	330	278	228	178
1	130	081	034	*013	*059	*104	*148	*192	*235	*277
2	$+ 10^{-2}\times$ 0.0319	360	400	440	479	517	555	592	628	664
3	699	734	767	801	833	865	897	928	958	988
4	.1017	045	073	101	128	154	180	205	230	254
5	278	301	324	346	368	389	410	430	450	470
6	488	507	525	542	560	576	592	608	624	639
7	653	667	681	694	707	720	732	744	756	767
8	777	788	798	807	817	826	834	843	851	858
9	866	873	879	886	892	898	903	908	913	918
7.0	922	926	930	933	937	940	942	945	947	949
1	951	952	954	955	956	956	957	957	957	956
2	956	955	954	953	952	950	949	947	945	943
3	940	938	935	932	929	926	922	919	915	911
4	907	903	899	895	890	885	880	875	870	865
5	860	854	849	843	837	832	826	819	813	807
6	800	794	787	781	774	767	760	753	746	739
7	731	724	717	709	701	694	686	678	670	663
8	655	647	639	630	622	614	606	597	589	581
9	572	564	555	547	538	529	521	512	503	495
8.0	486	477	468	459	450	442	433	424	415	406
1	397	388	379	370	361	352	343	334	325	315
2	306	297	288	279	270	261	252	243	234	225
3	216	207	198	189	180	171	162	153	144	135
4	126	117	108	099	090	081	072	064	055	046
5	037	029	020	011	0025	*9939	*9853	*9767	*9681	*9596
6	$+ 10^{-2}\times$ 0.9511	426	341	257	173	089	006	*923	*840	*757
7	.8675	593	512	430	350	269	189	109	029	*950
8	.7871	793	715	637	559	482	406	329	253	178
9	102	028	*953	*879	*805	*732	*659	*587	*515	*443
9.0	.6372	301	230	160	090	021	*952	*884	*816	*748
1	.5681	614	547	481	416	350	286	221	157	094
2	030	*968	*905	*844	*782	*721	*660	*600	*540	*481
3	.4422	364	305	248	190	133	077	021	*965	*910
4	.3855	801	747	694	640	588	535	483	432	381
5	330	280	230	181	132	083	035	*987	*940	*893
6	.2846	800	754	709	664	619	575	531	487	444
7	402	359	317	276	235	194	154	114	074	035
8	.1996	957	919	882	844	807	771	734	698	663
9	628	593	558	524	490	457	424	391	358	326
10.0	295	263	232	201	171	141	111	082	053	024

kei x

x	0	1	2	3	4	5	6	7	8	9
5.0	+ 10⁻²× 1.119	118	117	116	115	113	112	110	109	107
1	105	103	101	099	097	095	092	090	087	085
2	082	079	077	074	071	068	064	061	058	055
3	051	048	044	041	037	033	030	026	022	018
4	014	010	006	0017	*9975	*9933	*9891	*9848	*9804	*9761
5	0.9716	672	627	581	536	490	443	397	350	303
6	255	207	159	111	062	013	*964	*915	*865	*816
7	.8766	716	665	615	564	514	462	412	360	309
8	258	206	155	103	051	*999	*947	*895	*843	*791
9	.7739	687	635	582	530	478	426	373	321	269
6.0	216	164	112	060	008	*956	*904	*852	*800	*748
1	.6696	644	593	541	490	438	387	336	285	234
2	183	132	081	031	*980	*930	*880	*830	*780	*730
3	.5681	631	582	533	484	435	386	338	290	242
4	194	146	098	051	004	*956	*910	*863	*816	*770
5	.4724	678	632	587	542	497	452	407	362	318
6	274	230	187	143	100	057	015	*972	*930	*888
7	.3846	804	763	722	681	640	600	560	520	480
8	440	401	362	323	285	246	208	170	133	096
9	058	022	*985	*948	*913	*876	*841	*805	*770	*735
7.0	.2700	666	632	598	564	530	497	464	431	399
1	366	334	303	271	240	209	178	147	117	087
2	057	027	*998	*968	*939	*911	*882	*854	*826	*798
3	.1770	743	716	689	662	636	610	584	558	533
4	507	482	458	433	409	384	360	337	313	290
5	267	244	221	199	177	155	133	111	090	069
6	048	027	0067	*9864	*9663	*9463	*9266	*9071	*8878	*8687
7	+ 10⁻³ × 0.8498	8311	8126	7942	7761	7582	7404	7229	7055	6884
8	.6714	6546	6380	6215	6053	5892	5734	5577	5422	5268
9	.5117	4967	4819	4672	4528	4385	4244	4104	3966	3830
8.0	.3696	563	432	302	174	048	*923	*800	*679	*559
1	.2440	323	208	094	*982	*871	*762	*654	*547	*443
2	.1339	237	136	037	*939	*843	*748	*654	*562	*471
3	.0381	293	206	120	035	*048	*130	*210	*290	*368
4	− 10⁻³ × 0.0445	521	595	668	741	812	881	950	*017	*084
5	.1149	213	276	338	399	459	517	575	632	687
6	742	795	848	899	950	999	*048	*096	*142	*188
7	.2233	277	320	362	403	444	483	522	560	596
8	632	668	702	736	769	801	832	862	892	921
9	949	977	*003	*029	*055	*079	*103	*126	*149	*170
9.0	.3192	212	232	251	270	287	305	321	338	353
1	368	382	396	409	422	434	445	456	467	476
2	486	495	503	511	518	525	531	537	543	548
3	552	556	560	563	566	568	570	572	573	574
4	574	574	574	573	572	570	568	566	564	561
5	557	554	550	546	541	536	531	526	520	514
6	508	501	494	487	480	472	464	456	448	439
7	430	421	412	402	392	383	372	362	351	340
8	329	318	307	297	284	272	260	247	235	223
9	210	197	184	171	158	144	131	117	103	089
10.0	075	061	047	032	018	003	*989	*974	*959	*944

THOMSON FUNCTIONS

ker' x

x	0	1	2	3	4	5	6	7	8	9
0.0	− ∞	100.00	49.99	33.32	24.98	19.98	16.64	14.26	12.47	11.076
1	− 9.961	9.048	8.287	7.642	7.088	6.608	6.188	5.817	5.486	5.190
2	− 4.923	681	461	260	075	*905	*747	*601	*465	*338
3	− 3.220	109	004	*906	*814	*726	*643	*565	*490	*420
4	− 2.352	288	226	168	112	058	006	*957	*909	*864
5	− 1.820	778	737	698	660	623	588	553	520	488
6	457	426	397	369	341	314	288	263	238	214
7	191	168	146	124	103	083	063	043	024	0056
8	− 0.9873	9695	9521	9351	9185	9022	8863	8707	8554	8405
9	− 0.8259	8115	7975	7837	7702	7570	7440	7313	7189	7066
1.0	− 0.6946	828	713	599	487	378	271	165	061	*959
1	− 0.5859	761	664	569	475	383	293	204	117	031
2	− 0.4946	863	781	701	622	544	467	392	317	244
3	172	101	032	*963	*895	*829	*763	*699	*635	*572
4	− 0.3511	450	390	331	273	216	159	104	049	*995
5	− 0.2942	889	838	787	737	688	639	591	544	497
6	451	406	361	317	274	231	189	148	107	067
7	027	*988	*949	*911	*873	*837	*800	*764	*729	*694
8	− 0.1659	626	592	559	527	495	463	432	401	371
9	341	312	283	254	226	199	171	144	118	092
2.0	066	041	0156	*9910	*9667	*9427	*9192	*8959	*8730	*8505
1	− $10^{-1} \times$ 0.8282	8063	7848	7635	7426	7219	7016	6816	6619	6425
2	.6234	6045	5860	5677	5497	5320	5146	4974	4805	4639
3	.4475	4313	4155	3998	3844	3693	3544	3397	3253	3111
4	.2971	834	698	565	434	306	179	054	*932	*811
5	.1693	576	462	349	239	130	023	*918	*815	*713
6	.0614	516	419	325	232	141	051	*036	*123	*207
7	+ $10^{-1} \times$ 0.0290	372	452	531	608	683	757	830	901	971
8	.1040	107	173	237	301	363	423	483	541	598
9	653	708	761	814	865	914	963	*011	*058	*103
3.0	.2148	191	233	275	315	355	393	431	467	503
1	537	571	604	636	667	697	727	755	783	810
2	836	861	886	910	933	955	977	997	*017	*037
3	.3056	074	091	108	124	139	154	168	181	194
4	207	218	229	240	250	260	268	277	285	292
5	299	305	311	316	321	326	330	333	336	339
6	341	343	344	345	345	345	345	345	343	342
7	340	338	336	333	330	326	322	318	314	309
8	304	299	293	287	281	274	268	261	253	246
9	238	230	222	213	205	196	187	177	168	158
4.0	148	138	127	117	106	095	084	073	061	050
1	038	026	014	002	*990	*977	*965	*952	*939	*926
2	.2913	900	887	873	860	846	833	819	805	791
3	777	763	748	734	720	705	691	676	661	647
4	632	617	602	587	572	557	542	527	512	497
5	481	466	451	436	420	405	390	374	359	343
6	328	312	297	282	266	251	235	220	204	189
7	173	158	142	127	112	096	081	065	050	035
8	019	004	*989	*974	*958	*943	*928	*913	*898	*883
9	.1868	853	838	823	808	793	778	763	749	734
5.0	719	705	690	676	661	647	632	618	604	590

kei′ x

x	0	1	2	3	4	5	6	7	8	9
0.0	.0000	261	453	618	767	903	*029	*146	*257	*361
1	.1460	553	643	728	809	886	961	*032	*101	*166
2	.2229	290	348	404	458	510	560	609	655	700
3	743	784	824	863	900	936	970	*003	*035	*066
4	.3095	123	151	177	202	226	249	271	292	313
5	332	351	368	385	401	416	431	445	458	470
6	482	493	503	513	522	530	538	545	552	558
7	563	568	573	576	580	583	585	587	589	590
8	590	591	590	590	589	587	585	583	581	578
9	574	571	567	563	558	553	548	542	536	530
1.0	524	517	510	503	495	488	480	471	463	454
1	445	436	427	417	407	397	387	377	366	356
2	345	334	322	311	300	288	276	264	252	240
3	227	215	202	189	176	163	150	137	123	110
4	096	083	069	055	041	027	013	*999	*985	*970
5	.2956	942	927	913	898	883	869	854	839	824
6	809	794	779	764	749	734	719	703	688	673
7	658	642	627	612	597	581	566	551	535	520
8	504	489	474	458	443	427	412	397	381	366
9	351	335	320	305	289	274	259	244	228	213
2.0	198	183	168	153	138	123	108	093	078	063
1	048	033	018	003	*989	*974	*959	*945	*930	*916
2	.1901	887	872	858	844	829	815	801	787	773
3	759	745	731	717	703	689	675	662	648	635
4	621	608	594	581	568	554	541	528	515	502
5	489	476	463	450	438	425	412	400	387	375
6	363	350	338	326	314	302	290	278	266	254
7	243	231	219	208	196	185	174	162	151	140
8	129	118	107	096	085	074	064	053	042	032
9	021	011	0007	*9904	*9802	*9701	*9600	*9500	*9401	*9302
3.0	$10^{-1} \times$ 0.9204	107	010	*914	*819	*724	*630	*536	*443	*351
1	.8259	168	078	*988	*899	*811	*723	*635	*549	*463
2	.7378	293	209	125	042	*960	*878	*797	*717	*637
3	.6558	479	401	324	247	171	095	020	*946	*872
4	.5799	726	654	583	512	441	372	302	234	166
5	098	031	*965	*899	*834	*769	*705	*641	*578	*516
6	.4454	393	332	271	211	152	093	035	*977	*920
7	.3864	807	752	697	642	588	534	481	429	376
8	325	274	223	173	123	074	025	*977	*929	*882
9	.2835	788	742	697	652	607	563	519	476	433
4.0	391	349	308	267	226	186	146	106	067	029
1	.1991	953	916	879	842	806	770	735	700	666
2	631	598	564	531	498	466	434	403	371	341
3	310	280	250	221	192	163	135	106	079	051
4	0243	*9976	*9712	*9451	*9194	*8940	*8689	*8441	*8196	*7954
5	$+ 10^{-2} \times$ 0.7715	7480	7247	7018	6791	6567	6347	6129	5914	5702
6	.5492	5286	5082	4881	4683	4487	4295	4104	3917	3732
7	.3550	3370	3193	3018	2846	2676	2509	2345	2182	2022
8	.1865	710	557	406	258	112	*968	*827	*687	*550
9	.0415	282	152	023	*103	*228	*350	*471	*589	*706
5.0	$- 10^{-2} \times$ 0.0820	932	*043	*152	*259	*363	*467	*568	*667	*765

THOMSON FUNCTIONS

ker′ x

x	0	1	2	3	4	5	6	7	8	9
5.0	+ 10⁻¹× 0.1719	705	690	676	661	647	632	618	604	590
1	575	561	547	533	519	505	492	478	464	450
2	437	423	410	396	383	370	356	343	330	317
3	304	291	278	265	253	240	227	215	202	190
4	177	165	153	141	129	117	105	093	081	069
5	058	046	034	023	012	0003	*9890	*9779	*9667	*9557
6	+ 10⁻²× 0.9447	338	230	122	015	*909	*803	*698	*594	*491
7	.8388	286	185	084	*984	*885	*787	*689	*592	*495
8	.7400	305	210	117	024	*932	*840	*749	*659	*570
9	.6481	393	306	219	133	048	*963	*879	*796	*714
6.0	.5632	551	470	390	311	232	154	077	001	*925
1	.4850	775	701	628	555	483	412	341	271	202
2	133	065	*997	*930	*864	*798	*734	*669	*605	*542
3	.3479	417	356	295	235	175	116	058	000	*942
4	.2885	829	773	718	664	610	557	504	452	400
5	349	298	248	199	150	101	054	006	*959	*913
6	.1867	822	777	733	689	646	603	560	519	477
7	437	396	356	317	278	239	201	164	127	090
8	054	0183	*9830	*9481	*9137	*8798	*8462	*8131	*7805	*7482
9	+ 10⁻³× 0.7164	6850	6540	6234	5932	5634	5340	5051	4765	4483
7.0	.4205	3931	3661	3394	3132	2873	2617	2366	2118	1873
1	.1633	1396	1162	0932	0705	0482	0262	0046	*0168	*0377
2	− 10⁻³× 0.0584	0787	0987	1184	1377	1568	1755	1940	2121	2299
3	.2474	2646	2815	2982	3145	3306	3463	3618	3770	3920
4	.4066	210	351	490	626	759	890	*018	*144	*267
5	.5388	506	622	735	847	955	*062	*166	*268	*367
6	.6465	560	653	744	833	919	*004	*086	*167	*245
7	.7322	396	469	539	608	675	740	803	864	924
8	982	*038	*092	*145	*196	*245	*292	*338	*383	*426
9	.8467	506	545	581	616	650	682	713	743	771
8.0	797	823	846	869	890	910	929	947	963	978
1	992	*005	*016	*027	*036	*044	*051	*057	*062	*066
2	.9069	071	072	071	070	068	065	061	056	051
3	044	036	028	019	009	*998	*986	*974	*961	*947
4	.8932	916	900	883	866	848	829	809	789	768
5	747	725	702	679	655	630	605	580	554	527
6	500	473	445	416	387	358	328	298	267	236
7	204	172	140	107	074	041	007	*973	*938	*903
8	.7868	833	797	761	725	688	651	614	577	539
9	502	464	425	387	348	309	270	231	192	152
9.0	112	072	032	*992	*952	*911	*871	*830	*789	*748
1	.6707	666	625	584	543	501	460	418	377	335
2	293	252	210	168	126	084	043	001	*959	*917
3	.5875	833	792	750	708	666	624	583	541	499
4	458	416	375	333	292	251	210	168	127	086
5	045	005	*964	*923	*883	*842	*802	*761	*721	*681
6	.4641	601	562	522	482	443	404	365	326	287
7	248	209	171	133	094	056	018	*981	*943	*906
8	.3868	831	794	757	721	684	648	611	575	540
9	504	468	433	398	363	328	293	258	224	190
10.0	156	122	089	055	022	*989	*956	*923	*890	*858

kei′x

x	0	1	2	3	4	5	6	7	8	9
5.0	− 10⁻²× 0.0820	932	*043	*152	*259	*363	*467	*568	*667	*765
1	.1861	955	*047	*138	*227	*314	*400	*484	*566	*647
2	.2726	804	880	954	*027	*098	*168	*237	*304	*369
3	.3433	496	558	617	676	733	789	844	897	949
4	.4000	049	097	144	190	235	278	320	361	401
5	440	478	514	550	584	618	650	681	712	741
6	769	797	823	848	873	896	919	941	961	981
7	.5000	019	036	052	068	083	097	111	123	135
8	146	156	166	174	183	190	197	203	208	213
9	217	220	223	225	227	228	228	228	227	226
6.0	224	221	218	215	211	206	201	196	190	183
1	176	169	161	153	144	135	125	115	105	094
2	083	071	059	047	034	021	008	*994	*980	*966
3	.4951	936	921	905	889	873	857	840	823	806
4	788	770	752	734	716	697	678	659	639	620
5	600	580	560	540	519	498	478	456	435	414
6	393	371	349	327	305	283	261	239	216	193
7	171	148	125	102	079	056	033	009	*986	*962
8	.3939	915	892	868	844	820	796	773	749	725
9	701	677	653	628	604	580	556	532	508	484
7.0	460	435	411	387	363	339	315	290	266	242
1	218	194	170	146	122	098	075	051	027	003
2	.2979	956	932	909	885	862	838	815	791	768
3	745	722	699	676	653	630	607	584	562	539
4	517	494	472	450	427	405	383	361	339	318
5	296	274	253	231	210	189	168	146	125	105
6	084	063	043	022	002	*981	*961	*941	*921	*901
7	.1881	862	842	822	803	784	765	745	726	708
8	689	670	652	633	615	597	579	561	543	525
9	507	490	472	455	437	420	403	386	370	353
8.0	336	320	303	287	271	255	239	223	208	192
1	177	161	146	131	116	101	086	071	057	042
2	028	0136	*9995	*9854	*9715	*9577	*9440	*9303	*9168	*9035
3	− 10⁻³× 0.8902	770	639	510	381	254	127	002	*878	*754
4	.7632	511	391	272	154	037	*921	*806	*692	*579
5	.6467	356	247	138	030	*923	*817	*713	*609	*506
6	.5404	303	203	104	006	*909	*813	*718	*624	*530
7	.4438	347	256	167	078	*990	*904	*818	*733	*649
8	.3565	483	402	321	241	163	085	008	*931	*856
9	.2781	708	635	563	491	421	351	282	214	147
9.0	081	015	*950	*886	*823	*760	*699	*638	*577	*518
1	.1459	401	344	287	231	176	122	068	0149	*9626
2	− 10⁻⁴× 0.9109	8600	8097	7601	7112	6629	6153	5684	5221	4764
3	.4314	3871	3434	3002	2578	2159	1746	1340	0939	0545
4	.0156	*0227	*0604	*0975	*1341	*1700	*2054	*2403	*2746	*3084
5	+ 10⁻⁴× 0.3416	3743	4064	4380	4691	4997	5297	5593	5883	6168
6	.6448	6724	6994	7260	7521	7777	8029	8276	8518	8756
7	.8989	9217	9442	9662	9877	*0088	*030	*050	*070	*089
8	+ 10⁻³× 0.1108	127	145	163	180	197	214	230	246	262
9	277	292	306	320	334	347	360	373	385	397
10.0	409	421	432	442	453	463	473	482	491	500

ELLIPTIC INTEGRALS

Formulas

1. *Definitions*

Elliptic integral of the first kind:

$$F(x, y) = \mathscr{F}(k, y) = \int_0^y \frac{ds}{\sqrt{1 - \sin^2 x \sin^2 s}} = \int_0^{\sin y} \frac{dt}{\sqrt{1 - t^2} \sqrt{1 - k^2 t^2}}$$

Elliptic integral of the second kind:

$$E(x, y) = \mathscr{E}(k, y) = \int_0^y \sqrt{1 - \sin^2 x \sin^2 s}\; ds = \int_0^{\sin y} \sqrt{\frac{1 - k^2 t^2}{1 - t^2}}\; dt$$

with $k = \sin x$.

Usually the symbols F and E are applied indiscriminately to denote $\mathscr{F}$ and $\mathscr{E}$ as well.

2. *Complete integrals*

$$\mathscr{F}(k, 90°) = \mathscr{F}(k, \pi/2) = \mathsf{K}(k),$$

$$\mathscr{E}(k, 90°) = \mathscr{E}(k, \pi/2) = \mathsf{E}(k)$$

$$\mathsf{K}(k) = \int_0^1 \frac{dt}{\sqrt{1 - t^2} \sqrt{1 - k^2 t^2}} \qquad \mathsf{E}(k) = \int_0^1 \sqrt{\frac{1 - k^2 t^2}{1 - t^2}}\; dt$$

Power series for $k \ll 1$:

$$\mathsf{K}(k) = \frac{\pi}{2} \left[1 + \left(\frac{1}{2}\right)^2 k^2 + \left(\frac{1 \cdot 3}{2 \cdot 4}\right)^2 k^4 + \left(\frac{1 \cdot 3 \cdot 5}{2 \cdot 4 \cdot 6}\right)^2 k^6 + \dots \right]$$

$$\mathsf{E}(k) = \frac{\pi}{2} \left[1 - \frac{1}{2^2} k^2 - \frac{1^2 \cdot 3}{2^2 \cdot 4^2} k^4 - \frac{1^2 \cdot 3^2 \cdot 5}{2^2 \cdot 4^2 \cdot 6^2} k^6 - \dots \right]$$

Power series for $k \approx 1$, $k' = \sqrt{1 - k^2}$:

$$K(k) = -\left[\left(\frac{1}{2}\right)^2 k'^2 + \left(\frac{1 \cdot 3}{2 \cdot 4}\right)^2 \left(\frac{2}{1 \cdot 2} + \frac{2}{3 \cdot 4}\right) k'^4 + \right.$$

$$+ \left(\frac{1 \cdot 3 \cdot 5}{2 \cdot 4 \cdot 6}\right)^2 \left(\frac{2}{1 \cdot 2} + \frac{2}{3 \cdot 4} + \frac{2}{5 \cdot 6}\right) k'^6 + \cdots \right]$$

$$+ \ln(4/k') \left[1 + \left(\frac{1}{2}\right)^2 k'^2 + \left(\frac{1 \cdot 3}{2 \cdot 4}\right)^2 k'^4 + \left(\frac{1 \cdot 3 \cdot 5}{2 \cdot 4 \cdot 6}\right)^2 k'^6 + \cdots \right]$$

$$E(k) = 1 - \frac{1}{2}\left(\frac{1}{1 \cdot 2}\right) k'^2 - \frac{1^2 \cdot 3}{2^2 \cdot 4}\left(\frac{2}{1 \cdot 2} + \frac{1}{3 \cdot 4}\right) k'^4 - $$

$$- \frac{1^2 \cdot 3^2 \cdot 5}{2^2 \cdot 4^2 \cdot 6}\left(\frac{2}{1 \cdot 2} + \frac{2}{3 \cdot 4} + \frac{2}{5 \cdot 6}\right) k'^6 - \cdots$$

$$+ \ln(4/k') \left[\frac{1}{2} k'^2 + \frac{1^2 \cdot 3}{2^2 \cdot 4} k'^4 + \frac{1^2 \cdot 3^2 \cdot 5}{2^2 \cdot 4^2 \cdot 6} k'^6 + \cdots \right]$$

3. Special values

$$F(0, y) = E(0, y) = y, \qquad F(x, 0) = E(x, 0) = 0$$

$$F(90°, y) = \ln \tan(45° + y/2), \qquad E(90°, y) = \sin y$$

4. Argument y beyond the range of the tables

For integer n:

$$F(x, n\pi \pm y) = 2n F(x, 90°) \pm F(x, y)$$

$$E(x, n\pi \pm y) = 2n E(x, 90°) \pm E(x, y)$$

$$F(x, -y) = -F(x, y), \qquad E(x, -y) = -E(x, y)$$

5. Derivatives and integrals

$$\frac{\partial \mathscr{F}(k, y)}{\partial k} = \frac{\mathscr{E}(k, y)}{k(1 - k^2)} - \frac{\mathscr{F}(k, y)}{k} - \frac{k \sin y \cos y}{(1 - k^2)\sqrt{1 - k^2 \sin^2 y}}$$

$$\frac{\partial \mathscr{E}(k, y)}{\partial k} = \frac{\mathscr{E}(k, y) - \mathscr{F}(k, y)}{k}$$

$$\frac{d\mathsf{K}(k)}{dk} = \frac{\mathsf{E}(k)}{k\,(\mathrm{I} - k^2)} - \frac{\mathsf{K}(k)}{k}$$

$$\frac{d\mathsf{E}(k)}{dk} = \frac{\mathsf{E}(k) - \mathsf{K}(k)}{k}$$

$$\frac{\partial}{\partial k}\Big[\mathsf{K}(k)\,\mathscr{E}(k,y) - \mathsf{E}(k)\,\mathscr{F}(k,y)\Big] = \frac{k}{\mathrm{I} - k^2}\,\mathsf{E}(k)\,\frac{\cos y \sin y}{\sqrt{\mathrm{I} - k^2 \sin^2 y}}$$

$$\int \mathscr{F}(k,y)\,k\,dk = \mathscr{E}(k,y) - (\mathrm{I} - k^2)\,\mathscr{F}(k,y) - \left(\mathrm{I} - \sqrt{\mathrm{I} - k^2 \sin^2 y}\right)\cot y$$

6. *Definite integrals*

$$\int_0^z \frac{dt}{\sqrt{a^2 - t^2}\,\sqrt{b^2 - t^2}} = \frac{\mathrm{I}}{a}\,\mathrm{F}\,(x,y), \quad \sin x = \frac{b}{a}, \quad \sin y = \frac{z}{b}, \quad z < b < a$$

$$\int_z^a \frac{dt}{\sqrt{a^2 - t^2}\,\sqrt{t^2 - b^2}} = \frac{\mathrm{I}}{a}\,\mathrm{F}\,(x,y), \quad \cos x = \frac{b}{a}, \quad \sin^2 y = \frac{a^2 - z^2}{a^2 - b^2},$$
$$b < z < a$$

$$\int_z^\infty \frac{dt}{\sqrt{t^2 - a^2}\,\sqrt{t^2 - b^2}} = \frac{\mathrm{I}}{a}\,\mathrm{F}\,(x,y), \quad \sin x = \frac{b}{a}, \quad \sin y = \frac{a}{z}, \quad b < a < z$$

$$\int_z^a \frac{dt}{\sqrt{a^2 - t^2}\,\sqrt{b^2 + t^2}} = \frac{\mathrm{I}}{\sqrt{a^2 + b^2}}\,\mathrm{F}\,(x,y), \quad \tan x = \frac{a}{b}, \quad \cos y = \frac{z}{a}, \quad z < a$$

$$\int_a^z \frac{dt}{\sqrt{t^2 - a^2}\,\sqrt{b^2 + t^2}} = \frac{\mathrm{I}}{\sqrt{a^2 + b^2}}\,\mathrm{F}\,(x,y), \quad \tan x = \frac{b}{a}, \quad \cos y = \frac{a}{z}, \quad a < z$$

$$\int_0^z \frac{dt}{\sqrt{a^2 + t^2}\,\sqrt{b^2 + t^2}} = \frac{\mathrm{I}}{a}\,\mathrm{F}\,(x,y), \quad \cos x = \frac{b}{a}, \quad \tan y = \frac{z}{b}, \quad b < a$$

$$\int_0^z \sqrt{\frac{a^2 - t^2}{b^2 - t^2}}\,dt = a\,\mathrm{E}\,(x,y), \quad \sin x = \frac{b}{a}, \quad \sin y = \frac{z}{b}, \quad z < b < a$$

$$\int_0^z \sqrt{\frac{a^2 - t^2}{b^2 - t^2}}\,dt = b\,\mathrm{E}\,(x,y) - \frac{b^2 - a^2}{b}\,\mathrm{F}\,(x,y), \quad \sin x = \frac{a}{b}, \quad \sin y = \frac{z}{a},$$
$$z < a < b$$

$$\int_z^b \sqrt{\frac{t^2 - a^2}{b^2 - t^2}}\, dt = b\, \mathrm{E}\,(x, y) - \frac{a^2}{b}\, \mathrm{F}\,(x, y), \quad \cos x = \frac{a}{b}, \quad \sin^2 y = \frac{b^2 - z^2}{b^2 - a^2},$$

$$a < z < b$$

$$\int_z^a \sqrt{\frac{a^2 - t^2}{t^2 - b^2}}\, dt = a\, [\mathrm{F}\,(x, y) - \mathrm{E}\,(x, y)], \quad \cos x = \frac{b}{a}, \quad \sin^2 y = \frac{a^2 - z^2}{a^2 - b^2},$$

$$b < z < a$$

$$\int_z^a \sqrt{\frac{a^2 - t^2}{b^2 + t^2}}\, dt = \sqrt{a^2 + b^2}\, [\mathrm{F}\,(x, y) - \mathrm{E}\,(x, y)], \quad \tan x = \frac{a}{b}, \quad \cos y = \frac{z}{a}$$

$$z < a$$

$$\int_z^b \sqrt{\frac{a^2 + t^2}{b^2 - t^2}}\, dt = \sqrt{a^2 + b^2}\, \mathrm{E}\,(x, y), \quad \tan x = \frac{b}{a}, \quad \cos y = \frac{z}{b}, \quad z < b$$

$$\int_z^1 \frac{dt}{\sqrt{1 - t^4}} = \frac{1}{\sqrt{2}}\, \mathrm{F}\,(45°, y), \quad \cos y = z, \quad z < 1$$

$$\int_1^z \frac{dt}{\sqrt{t^4 - 1}} = \frac{1}{\sqrt{2}}\, \mathrm{F}\,(45°, y), \quad \cos y = \frac{1}{z}, \quad 1 < z$$

$$\int_0^z \frac{dt}{\sqrt{1 + t^4}} = \tfrac{1}{2}\, \mathrm{F}\,(45°, y), \quad \sin y = \frac{2z}{1 + z^2}, \quad z < 1$$

$$\int_z^\infty \frac{dt}{\sqrt{1 + t^4}} = \tfrac{1}{2}\, \mathrm{F}\,(45°, y), \quad \sin y = \frac{2z}{1 + z^2}, \quad 1 < z$$

$$\int_z^1 \frac{dt}{\sqrt{1 - t^3}} = \frac{1}{\sqrt[4]{3}}\, \mathrm{F}\,(75°, y), \quad \cos y = \frac{\sqrt{3} - 1 + z}{\sqrt{3} + 1 - z}, \quad z < 1$$

$$\int_z^\infty \frac{dt}{\sqrt{t^3 - 1}} = \frac{1}{\sqrt[4]{3}}\, \mathrm{F}\,(15°, y), \quad \cos y = \frac{z - 1 - \sqrt{3}}{z - 1 + \sqrt{3}}, \quad 1 < z$$

7. Elliptic integral of the third kind

The integral

$$\int_0^y \frac{ds}{(1 + c^2 \sin^2 s) \sqrt{1 - k^2 \sin^2 s}} = \int_0^{\sin y} \frac{dt}{(1 + c^2 t^2) \sqrt{1 - t^2} \sqrt{1 - k^2 t^2}}$$

is called " elliptic integral of the third kind ". The complete integral (i.e. with the upper limit $y = 90°$) may be expressed by complete and incomplete integrals of the first and second kinds as follows:

$$\int_0^1 \frac{dt}{(1 + c^2 t^2) \sqrt{1 - t^2} \sqrt{1 - k^2 t^2}} = \frac{F(x, 90°)}{1 + c^2} + \frac{c}{\sqrt{1 + c^2} \sqrt{c^2 + k^2}} \left[\frac{\pi}{2} - \right.$$

$$- F(x, 90°) E(90° - x, y) - E(x, 90°) F(90° - x, y) +$$

$$\left. + F(x, 90°) F(90° - x, y) \right]$$

with $\sin x = k$, $\cot y = c$, valid for $\quad c^2 > 0$, $k^2 < 1$;

$$\int_0^1 \frac{dt}{(1 - c^2 t^2) \sqrt{1 - t^2} \sqrt{1 - k^2 t^2}} = F(x, 90°) +$$

$$+ \frac{c}{\sqrt{1 - c^2} \sqrt{k^2 - c^2}} [F(x, 90°) E(x, y) - E(x, 90°) F(x, y)]$$

with $\sin x = k$, $\sin y = \dfrac{c}{k}$, valid for $0 < c < k < 1$;

$$\int_0^1 \frac{dt}{(1 - c^2 t^2) \sqrt{1 - t^2} \sqrt{1 - k^2 t^2}} = F(x, 90°) + \frac{c}{\sqrt{1 - c^2} \sqrt{c^2 - k^2}} \left[\frac{\pi}{2} - \right.$$

$$- F(x, 90°) E(90° - x, y) - E(x, 90°) F(90° - x, y) +$$

$$\left. + F(x, 90°) F(90° - x, y) \right]$$

with $\sin x = k$, $\sin^2 y = \dfrac{1 - c^2}{1 - k^2}$, valid for $0 < k < c < 1$.

8. *Bibliography*

A. M. LEGENDRE: *Exercices de calcul intégral*, vol. 3, Paris, 1816, Table IX, and *Traité des fonctions elliptiques*, vol. 2, Paris, 1826, Table IX. Recent reprints: *A. M. Legendres Tafeln der elliptischen Normalintegrale*, herausgeg. von F. Emde, Stuttgart, 1931; *Tables of the Complete and Incomplete Elliptic Integrals*, by K. Pearson, London, 1934.

$F(x, y)$, $E(x, y)$ with 9–10 dig. for $x, y = 0°\,(1°)\,90°$.

Author's notation: ϕ for y, $F(2°)$, $E(2°)$ for $F(2°, y)$, $E(2°, y)$.

For the correction of some errors in these tables see:
C. HEUMAN: *J. Math. Phys.*, vol. 20 (1941), pp. 143-144.

F (x, y)

y	x 0°	2°	4°	6°	8°	10°	12°	14°	16°	18°
0°	.0000	.0000	.0000	.0000	.0000	.0000	.0000	.0000	.0000	.0000
1°	175	175	175	175	175	175	175	175	175	175
2°	349	349	349	349	349	349	349	349	349	349
3°	524	524	524	524	524	524	524	524	524	524
4°	698	698	698	698	698	698	698	698	698	698
5°	873	873	873	873	873	873	873	873	873	873
6°	.1047	.1047	.1047	.1047	.1047	.1047	.1047	.1047	.1047	.1047
7°	222	222	222	222	222	222	222	222	222	222
8°	396	396	396	396	396	396	396	397	397	397
9°	571	571	571	571	571	571	571	571	571	571
10°	745	745	745	745	745	746	746	746	746	746
11°	920	920	920	920	920	920	920	921	921	921
12°	.2094	.2094	.2094	.2095	.2095	.2095	.2095	.2095	.2096	.2096
13°	269	269	269	269	269	270	270	270	270	271
14°	443	443	444	444	444	444	445	445	445	446
15°	618	618	618	618	619	619	619	620	620	621
16°	793	793	793	793	793	794	794	795	795	796
17°	967	967	967	968	968	968	969	970	970	971
18°	.3142	.3142	.3142	.3142	.3143	.3143	.3144	.3145	.3145	.3146
19°	316	316	316	317	317	318	319	320	321	322
20°	491	491	491	491	492	493	494	495	496	497
21°	665	665	666	666	667	668	669	670	671	673
22°	840	840	840	841	842	842	844	845	847	849
23°	.4014	.4014	.4015	.4015	.4016	.4017	.4019	.4020	.4022	.4024
24°	189	189	189	190	191	192	194	196	198	200
25°	363	363	364	365	366	367	369	371	374	376
26°	538	538	539	539	541	542	544	547	549	552
27°	712	713	713	714	716	717	720	722	725	728
28°	887	887	888	889	891	893	895	898	901	905
29°	.5061	.5062	.5062	.5064	.5065	.5068	.5070	.5074	.5077	.5081
30°	236	236	237	238	240	243	246	249	253	258
31°	411	411	412	413	415	418	421	425	430	435
32°	585	585	586	588	590	593	597	601	606	611
33°	760	760	761	763	765	769	773	777	782	788
34°	934	935	936	938	940	944	948	953	959	966
35°	.6109	.6109	.6110	.6113	.6116	.6119	.6124	.6129	.6136	.6143
36°	283	284	285	287	291	295	300	306	313	320
37°	458	458	460	462	466	470	476	482	489	498
38°	632	633	634	637	641	646	652	659	667	675
39°	807	807	809	812	816	821	828	835	844	853
40°	981	982	984	987	991	997	.7004	.7012	.7021	.7031
41°	.7156	.7157	.7159	.7162	.7167	.7173	180	188	198	210
42°	330	331	333	337	342	348	356	365	376	388
43°	505	506	508	512	517	524	532	542	554	566
44°	679	680	683	687	692	700	709	719	731	745
45°	854	855	857	862	868	876	885	896	909	924

F (x, y)

y	0°	2°	4°	6°	8°	10°	12°	14°	16°	18°
45°	.7854	.7855	.7857	.7862	.7868	.7876	.7885	.7896	.7909	.7924
46°	.8029	.8029	.8032	.8037	.8043	.8052	.8062	.8074	.8087	.8103
47°	203	204	207	212	219	227	238	251	265	282
48°	378	379	382	387	394	403	415	428	444	461
49°	552	553	556	562	570	579	591	606	622	640
50°	727	728	731	737	745	756	768	783	800	820
51°	901	902	906	912	921	932	945	961	979	.9000
52°	.9076	.9077	.9081	.9087	.9096	.9108	.9122	.9139	.9158	180
53°	250	252	256	262	272	284	299	316	337	360
54°	425	426	430	438	448	460	476	494	516	540
55°	599	601	605	613	623	637	653	672	695	720
56°	774	775	780	788	799	813	830	851	874	901
57°	948	950	955	963	975	989	1.0007	1.0029	1.0053	1.0081
58°	1.0123	1.0125	1.0130	1.0138	1.0150	1.0166	0185	021	023	026
59°	030	030	030	031	033	034	036	039	041	044
60°	047	047	048	049	050	052	054	056	059	062
61°	065	065	065	066	068	070	072	074	077	081
62°	082	082	083	084	085	087	089	092	095	099
63°	100	100	100	101	103	105	107	110	113	117
64°	117	117	118	119	121	123	125	128	131	135
65°	134	135	135	137	138	140	143	146	149	153
66°	152	152	153	154	156	158	161	164	167	171
67°	169	170	170	172	173	176	178	182	185	190
68°	187	187	188	189	191	193	196	199	203	208
69°	204	205	205	207	209	211	214	217	221	226
70°	222	222	223	224	226	229	232	235	239	244
71°	239	239	240	242	244	246	249	253	258	262
72°	257	257	258	259	261	264	267	271	276	281
73°	274	274	275	277	279	282	285	289	294	299
74°	292	292	293	294	297	299	303	307	312	317
75°	309	309	310	312	314	317	321	325	330	336
76°	326	327	328	329	332	335	339	343	348	354
77°	344	344	345	347	349	353	356	361	366	372
78°	361	362	363	365	367	370	374	379	384	390
79°	379	379	380	382	385	388	392	397	402	409
80°	396	397	398	400	402	406	410	415	420	427
81°	414	414	415	417	420	423	428	433	439	445
82°	431	432	433	435	437	441	445	451	457	464
83°	449	449	450	452	455	459	463	469	475	482
84°	466	466	468	470	473	477	481	487	493	500
85°	484	484	485	487	490	494	499	505	511	519
86°	501	501	503	505	508	512	517	523	529	537
87°	518	519	520	522	526	529	535	541	548	555
88°	536	536	538	540	543	547	553	559	566	574
89°	553	554	555	558	561	565	570	577	584	592
90°	571	571	573	575	578	583	588	595	602	610

F (x, y)

y	\[x] 18°	20°	22°	24°	26°	28°	30°	32°	34°	36°
0°	.0000	.0000	.0000	.0000	.0000	.0000	.0000	.0000	.0000	.0000
1°	175	175	175	175	175	175	175	175	175	175
2°	349	349	349	349	349	349	349	349	349	349
3°	524	524	524	524	524	524	524	524	524	524
4°	698	698	698	698	698	698	698	698	698	698
5°	873	873	873	873	873	873	873	873	873	873
6°	.1047	.1047	.1047	.1048	.1048	.1048	.1048	.1048	.1048	.1048
7°	222	222	222	222	222	222	222	223	223	223
8°	397	397	397	397	397	397	397	398	398	398
9°	571	572	572	572	572	572	572	573	573	573
10°	746	746	747	747	747	747	748	748	748	748
11°	921	921	922	922	922	922	923	923	924	924
12°	.2096	.2096	.2097	.2097	.2097	.2098	.2098	.2099	.2099	.2100
13°	271	271	272	272	273	273	274	274	275	276
14°	446	446	447	447	448	449	450	450	451	452
15°	621	621	622	623	624	625	625	626	627	628
16°	796	797	798	798	799	800	802	803	804	805
17°	971	972	973	974	975	977	978	979	981	982
18°	.3146	.3148	.3149	.3150	.3151	.3153	.3154	.3156	.3158	.3159
19°	322	323	325	326	328	329	331	333	335	337
20°	497	499	500	502	504	506	508	510	513	515
21°	673	675	676	679	681	683	685	688	691	693
22°	849	851	853	855	858	860	863	866	869	872
23°	.4024	.4027	.4029	.4032	.4035	.4038	.4041	.4044	.4048	.4051
24°	200	203	206	209	212	215	219	223	227	231
25°	376	379	382	386	389	393	397	402	406	411
26°	552	556	559	563	567	571	576	581	586	591
27°	728	732	736	740	745	750	755	761	766	772
28°	905	909	913	918	923	929	934	941	947	953
29°	.5081	.5086	.5091	.5096	.5102	.5108	.5114	.5121	.5128	.5135
30°	258	263	268	274	280	287	294	302	309	317
31°	435	440	446	453	460	467	475	483	491	500
32°	611	617	624	631	639	647	656	665	674	684
33°	788	795	802	810	818	827	837	847	857	868
34°	966	973	981	989	998	.6008	.6018	.6029	.6040	.6052
35°	.6143	.6151	.6159	.6168	.6178	189	200	212	224	237
36°	320	329	338	348	359	370	383	396	409	423
37°	498	507	517	528	540	552	565	579	594	609
38°	675	685	696	708	721	734	749	764	780	796
39°	853	864	876	889	902	917	932	949	966	984
40°	.7031	.7043	.7056	.7069	.7084	.7100	.7116	.7134	.7153	.7172
41°	210	222	235	250	266	283	301	320	340	361
42°	388	401	416	431	448	467	486	506	528	550
43°	566	580	596	613	631	651	671	693	716	740
44°	745	760	777	795	814	835	857	881	905	931
45°	924	940	958	977	998	.8020	.8044	.8069	.8095	.8123

F (x, y)

y	x									
	18°	20°	22°	24°	26°	28°	30°	32°	34°	36°
45°	.7924	.7940	.7958	.7977	.7998	.8020	.8044	.8069	.8095	.8123
46°	.8103	.8120	.8139	.8159	.8181	205	230	257	285	315
47°	282	300	320	342	365	391	418	446	476	508
48°	461	480	502	525	550	577	606	636	668	702
49°	640	661	683	708	735	763	794	826	860	896
50°	820	842	866	892	920	950	982	.9017	.9053	.9091
51°	.9000	.9023	.9048	.9075	.9105	.9137	.9172	208	247	287
52°	180	204	230	260	291	325	361	400	441	484
53°	360	385	413	444	477	513	551	592	635	681
54°	540	567	596	629	664	702	742	785	831	879
55°	720	748	779	814	851	890	933	979	1.0027	1.0078
56°	901	930	963	999	1.0038	1.0080	1.0125	1.0173	0223	028
57°	1.0081	1.0112	1.0147	1.0184	0225	027	032	037	042	048
58°	026	029	033	037	041	046	051	056	062	068
59°	044	048	051	056	060	065	070	076	082	088
60°	062	066	070	074	079	084	090	095	102	108
61°	081	084	088	093	098	103	109	115	122	129
62°	099	103	107	112	117	122	128	135	142	149
63°	117	121	125	130	136	142	148	155	162	169
64°	135	139	144	149	155	161	167	174	182	190
65°	153	158	162	168	174	180	187	194	202	211
66°	171	176	181	187	193	199	207	214	222	231
67°	190	194	200	205	212	219	226	234	243	252
68°	208	213	218	224	231	238	246	254	263	273
69°	226	231	237	243	250	257	266	274	284	294
70°	244	250	255	262	269	277	285	294	304	314
71°	262	268	274	281	288	296	305	314	325	335
72°	281	286	293	300	307	316	325	335	345	356
73°	299	305	311	319	327	335	345	355	366	377
74°	317	323	330	338	346	355	365	375	386	399
75°	336	342	349	357	365	374	385	395	407	420
76°	354	360	368	376	384	394	405	416	428	441
77°	372	379	386	395	404	414	424	436	449	462
78°	390	397	405	414	423	433	444	457	470	484
79°	409	416	424	433	442	453	465	477	490	505
80°	427	434	443	452	462	473	485	497	511	526
81°	445	453	461	471	481	492	505	518	532	548
82°	464	472	480	490	500	512	525	538	553	569
83°	482	490	499	509	520	532	545	559	574	591
84°	500	509	518	528	539	552	565	579	595	612
85°	519	527	537	547	559	571	585	600	616	634
86°	537	546	555	566	578	591	605	621	637	655
87°	555	564	574	585	597	611	625	641	658	677
88°	574	583	593	604	617	631	645	662	679	698
89°	592	601	612	623	636	650	666	682	700	720
90°	610	620	631	643	656	670	686	703	721	741

G

ELLIPTIC INTEGRALS

F (x, y)

y	36°	38°	40°	42°	44°	46°	48°	50°	52°	54°
0°	.0000	.0000	.0000	.0000	.0000	.0000	.0000	.0000	.0000	.0000
1°	175	175	175	175	175	175	175	175	175	175
2°	349	349	349	349	349	349	349	349	349	349
3°	524	524	524	524	524	524	524	524	524	524
4°	698	698	698	698	698	698	698	698	698	699
5°	873	873	873	873	873	873	873	873	873	873
6°	.1048	.1048	.1048	.1048	.1048	.1048	.1048	.1048	.1048	.1048
7°	223	223	223	223	223	223	223	224	224	224
8°	398	398	398	398	398	399	399	399	399	399
9°	573	573	573	574	574	574	574	575	575	575
10°	748	749	749	749	750	750	750	751	751	751
11°	924	924	925	925	926	926	926	927	927	928
12°	.2100	.2100	.2101	.2101	.2102	.2102	.2103	.2103	.2104	.2104
13°	276	276	277	278	278	279	280	280	281	282
14°	452	453	453	454	455	456	457	458	459	459
15°	628	629	630	631	632	634	635	636	637	638
16°	805	806	808	809	810	811	813	814	815	816
17°	982	984	985	987	988	990	991	993	994	996
18°	.3159	.3161	.3163	.3165	.3167	.3168	.3170	.3172	.3174	.3176
19°	337	339	341	343	346	348	350	352	354	356
20°	515	517	520	522	525	527	530	533	535	538
21°	693	696	699	702	705	708	711	714	717	720
22°	872	875	879	882	885	889	892	896	899	902
23°	.4051	.4055	.4059	.4063	.4066	.4070	.4074	.4078	.4082	.4086
24°	231	235	239	244	248	252	257	261	266	270
25°	411	415	420	425	430	435	440	446	451	456
26°	591	596	602	608	613	619	625	630	636	642
27°	772	778	784	790	797	803	810	816	823	829
28°	953	960	967	974	981	988	995	.5003	.5010	.5017
29°	.5135	.5143	.5150	.5158	.5166	.5174	.5182	190	198	206
30°	317	326	334	343	352	361	370	379	388	397
31°	500	510	519	529	538	548	558	568	578	588
32°	684	694	704	715	726	737	748	759	770	781
33°	868	879	890	902	914	926	938	950	962	974
34°	.6052	.6064	.6077	.6090	.6103	.6116	.6129	.6143	.6156	.6169
35°	237	251	264	278	293	307	322	336	351	366
36°	423	437	452	468	483	499	515	531	547	563
37°	609	625	641	658	675	692	710	727	745	763
38°	796	813	831	849	868	886	905	925	944	963
39°	984	.7002	.7021	.7041	.7061	.7082	.7102	.7123	.7144	.7165
40°	.7172	192	213	234	256	278	300	323	346	369
41°	361	382	405	428	451	475	500	524	549	574
42°	550	574	598	622	648	674	700	727	754	781
43°	740	765	791	818	845	874	902	931	960	989
44°	931	958	986	.8015	.8044	.8074	.8105	.8136	.8168	.8199
45°	.8123	.8152	.8181	212	244	276	310	343	377	411

F (x, y)

y	36°	38°	40°	42°	44°	46°	48°	50°	52°	54°
					x					
45°	.8123	.8152	.8181	.8212	.8244	.8276	.8310	.8343	.8377	.8411
46°	315	346	378	411	445	480	515	552	588	625
47°	508	541	575	611	647	684	723	761	801	840
48°	702	737	773	811	850	890	931	973	.9015	.9058
49°	896	934	972	.9013	.9055	.9097	.9141	.9186	231	277
50°	.9091	.9131	.9173	216	260	306	353	401	449	499
51°	287	329	374	419	467	516	566	617	669	722
52°	484	529	575	624	675	727	780	835	891	947
53°	681	729	778	830	884	939	997	1.0055	1.0115	1.0175
54°	879	929	982	1.0037	1.0094	1.0153	1.0214	0277	034	040
55°	1.0078	1.0131	1.0187	0245	031	037	043	050	057	064
56°	028	033	039	045	052	059	065	072	080	087
57°	048	054	060	066	073	080	088	095	103	111
58°	068	074	081	088	095	102	110	118	126	135
59°	088	095	102	109	116	124	133	141	150	159
60°	108	115	123	130	138	147	155	164	174	183
61°	129	136	144	152	160	169	178	188	198	208
62°	149	157	165	173	182	192	201	211	222	232
63°	169	177	186	195	204	214	224	235	246	258
64°	190	198	207	217	227	237	248	259	271	283
65°	211	219	229	239	249	260	271	283	296	308
66°	231	240	250	261	272	283	295	308	321	334
67°	252	262	272	283	294	306	319	332	346	360
68°	273	283	294	305	317	330	343	357	371	386
69°	294	304	315	327	340	353	367	382	397	413
70°	314	325	337	350	363	377	391	407	423	440
71°	335	347	359	372	386	401	416	432	449	467
72°	356	368	381	395	409	424	440	457	475	494
73°	377	390	403	417	432	448	465	483	502	521
74°	399	412	425	440	456	472	490	509	528	549
75°	420	433	448	463	479	497	515	535	555	577
76°	441	455	470	486	503	521	540	561	582	605
77°	462	477	492	509	527	545	565	587	609	633
78°	484	499	515	532	550	570	591	613	637	662
79°	505	521	537	555	574	595	616	639	664	690
80°	526	542	560	578	598	619	642	666	692	719
81°	548	564	582	601	622	644	668	693	719	748
82°	569	586	605	625	646	669	693	719	747	777
83°	591	608	628	648	670	694	719	746	775	806
84°	612	631	650	671	694	719	745	773	803	836
85°	634	653	673	695	718	744	771	800	831	865
86°	655	675	696	718	743	769	797	827	860	895
87°	677	697	718	742	767	794	823	854	888	924
88°	698	719	741	765	791	819	849	881	916	954
89°	720	741	764	789	815	844	875	908	945	984
90°	741	763	787	812	840	869	901	936	973	2.013

ELLIPTIC INTEGRALS

F (x, y)

y	54°	56°	58°	60°	62°	64°	66°	68°	70°	72°
0°	.0000	.0000	.0000	.0000	.0000	.0000	.0000	.0000	.0000	.0000
1°	175	175	175	175	175	175	175	175	175	175
2°	349	349	349	349	349	349	349	349	349	349
3°	524	524	524	524	524	524	524	524	524	524
4°	699	699	699	699	699	699	699	699	699	699
5°	873	873	873	873	874	874	874	874	874	874
6°	.1048	.1049	.1049	.1049	.1049	.1049	.1049	.1049	.1049	.1049
7°	224	224	224	224	224	224	224	224	224	224
8°	399	399	400	400	400	400	400	400	400	400
9°	575	575	575	576	576	576	576	576	577	577
10°	751	751	752	752	752	753	753	753	753	753
11°	928	928	928	929	929	929	930	930	930	931
12°	.2104	.2105	.2105	.2106	.2106	.2107	.2107	.2108	.2108	.2108
13°	282	282	283	284	284	285	285	286	286	287
14°	459	460	461	462	463	463	464	465	465	466
15°	638	639	640	641	642	642	643	644	645	645
16°	816	818	819	820	821	822	823	824	825	826
17°	996	997	999	.3000	.3001	.3003	.3004	.3005	.3006	.3007
18°	.3176	.3177	.3179	181	182	184	185	187	188	189
19°	356	358	360	362	364	366	368	369	371	372
20°	538	540	542	545	547	549	551	553	555	556
21°	720	722	725	728	730	733	735	738	740	742
22°	902	906	909	912	915	918	921	923	926	928
23°	.4086	.4090	.4093	.4097	.4100	.4104	.4107	.4110	.4113	.4115
24°	270	275	279	283	287	291	294	298	301	304
25°	456	460	465	470	474	479	483	487	490	494
26°	642	647	653	658	663	668	673	677	681	685
27°	829	835	841	847	853	859	864	869	873	878
28°	.5017	.5024	.5031	.5038	.5044	.5050	.5056	.5062	.5067	.5072
29°	206	214	222	229	237	244	250	257	262	268
30°	397	405	414	422	430	438	446	453	459	465
31°	588	598	607	617	626	634	643	651	658	665
32°	781	791	802	812	822	832	841	850	858	866
33°	974	986	998	.6010	.6021	.6031	.6042	.6051	.6060	.6069
34°	.6169	.6183	.6196	208	221	232	244	254	265	274
35°	366	380	395	408	422	435	448	460	471	481
36°	563	579	595	610	625	640	654	667	679	690
37°	763	780	797	814	830	846	861	876	890	902
38°	963	982	.7001	.7019	.7037	.7055	.7071	.7087	.7102	.7116
39°	.7165	.7186	207	227	246	265	284	301	318	333
40°	369	391	414	436	457	478	498	517	535	552
41°	574	598	623	647	670	693	715	736	756	774
42°	781	807	834	860	886	910	934	957	979	999
43°	989	.8018	.8047	.8075	.8103	.8130	.8156	.8181	.8204	.8226
44°	.8199	231	262	293	323	352	381	408	433	457
45°	411	445	479	512	545	577	608	637	665	692

F (x, y)

y	54°	56°	58°	60°	62°	64°	66°	68°	70°	72°
					x					
45°	.8411	.8445	.8479	.8512	.8545	.8577	.8608	.8637	.8665	.8692
46°	625	661	698	734	770	804	838	870	900	929
47°	840	880	919	958	997	.9035	.9071	.9106	.9139	.9170
48°	.9058	.9100	.9143	.9185	.9227	268	307	345	381	415
49°	277	323	369	415	460	504	546	588	627	664
50°	499	548	597	647	695	743	789	834	876	916
51°	722	775	828	881	934	985	1.0035	1.0083	1.0130	1.0173
52°	947	1.0004	1.0062	1.0118	1.0175	1.0230	0285	034	039	043
53°	1.0175	0236	030	036	042	048	054	059	065	070
54°	040	047	054	060	067	073	080	086	092	097
55°	064	071	078	085	092	099	106	112	119	125
56°	087	095	102	110	117	125	132	139	146	153
57°	111	119	127	135	143	151	159	167	174	181
58°	135	143	152	160	169	178	186	195	203	211
59°	159	168	177	186	196	205	214	223	232	241
60°	183	193	203	213	223	233	243	252	262	271
61°	208	218	228	239	250	261	271	282	292	302
62°	232	243	255	266	278	289	301	312	323	334
63°	258	269	281	293	306	318	330	343	355	366
64°	283	295	308	321	334	347	361	374	387	400
65°	308	322	335	349	363	377	392	406	420	434
66°	334	348	363	377	392	408	423	438	454	468
67°	360	375	390	406	422	438	455	472	488	504
68°	386	402	418	435	452	470	488	505	523	541
69°	413	430	447	465	483	502	521	540	559	578
70°	440	457	476	494	514	534	554	575	596	617
71°	467	485	505	525	545	567	589	611	634	656
72°	494	513	534	555	577	600	624	648	672	696
73°	521	542	564	586	610	634	659	685	711	738
74°	549	571	594	618	642	668	695	723	752	780
75°	577	600	624	649	676	703	732	762	793	824
76°	605	629	654	681	709	739	770	802	835	869
77°	633	659	685	714	743	775	808	842	878	915
78°	662	688	716	746	778	811	846	883	922	962
79°	690	718	748	779	813	848	885	925	966	2.010
80°	719	748	779	813	848	885	925	967	2.012	059
81°	748	779	811	846	883	923	965	2.010	058	109
82°	777	809	843	880	919	961	2.006	054	106	161
83°	806	840	876	914	955	2.000	047	098	154	213
84°	836	871	908	948	992	038	089	143	202	267
85°	865	901	941	983	2.028	077	131	189	252	321
86°	895	932	973	2.017	065	117	173	234	302	376
87°	924	964	2.006	052	102	156	215	280	352	431
88°	954	995	039	087	139	196	258	327	403	487
89°	984	2.026	072	122	176	236	301	373	454	543
90°	2.013	057	105	157	213	275	344	420	505	600

F (x, y)

y	72°	74°	76°	78°	80°	82°	84°	86°	88°	90°
0°	.0000	.0000	.0000	.0000	.0000	.0000	.0000	.0000	.0000	.0000
1°	175	175	175	175	175	175	175	175	175	175
2°	349	349	349	349	349	349	349	349	349	349
3°	524	524	524	524	524	524	524	524	524	524
4°	699	699	699	699	699	699	699	699	699	699
5°	874	874	874	874	874	874	874	874	874	874
6°	.1049	.1049	.1049	.1049	.1049	.1049	.1049	.1049	.1049	.1049
7°	224	225	225	225	225	225	225	225	225	225
8°	400	400	401	401	401	401	401	401	401	401
9°	577	577	577	577	577	577	577	577	577	577
10°	753	754	754	754	754	754	754	754	754	754
11°	931	931	931	931	931	932	932	932	932	932
12°	.2108	.2109	.2109	.2109	.2109	.2110	.2110	.2110	.2110	.2110
13°	287	287	287	288	288	288	288	289	289	289
14°	466	466	467	467	467	468	468	468	468	468
15°	645	646	647	647	647	648	648	648	648	648
16°	826	827	827	828	828	829	829	829	829	830
17°	.3007	.3008	.3009	.3010	.3010	.3011	.3011	.3011	.3012	.3012
18°	189	190	191	192	193	194	194	194	195	195
19°	372	374	375	376	377	377	378	378	379	379
20°	556	558	559	560	561	562	563	563	564	564
21°	742	743	745	746	747	748	749	750	750	750
22°	928	930	932	933	935	936	937	937	938	938
23°	.4115	.4117	.4120	.4121	.4123	.4124	.4125	.4126	.4126	.4127
24°	304	306	309	311	313	314	315	316	317	317
25°	494	497	499	502	504	506	507	508	509	509
26°	685	688	692	694	697	699	700	701	702	702
27°	878	882	885	888	891	893	895	896	897	897
28°	.5072	.5076	.5080	.5084	.5087	.5089	.5091	.5093	.5094	.5094
29°	268	273	277	281	285	287	290	291	292	293
30°	465	471	476	480	484	487	490	492	493	493
31°	665	671	677	682	686	689	692	694	695	696
32°	866	873	879	885	889	893	896	899	900	900
33°	.6069	.6077	.6084	.6090	.6095	.6099	.6103	.6105	.6107	.6107
34°	274	283	290	297	303	308	312	314	316	317
35°	481	491	499	507	513	519	523	526	528	528
36°	690	701	710	719	726	732	737	740	742	743
37°	902	914	924	933	941	948	953	957	959	960
38°	.7116	.7129	.7140	.7151	.7159	.7167	.7172	.7177	.7179	.7180
39°	333	347	359	371	380	388	395	399	402	403
40°	552	567	581	594	604	613	620	625	628	629
41°	774	791	806	820	831	841	849	854	858	859
42°	999	.8017	.8034	.8049	.8062	.8072	.8081	.8087	.8090	.8092
43°	.8226	247	265	281	295	307	316	323	327	328
44°	457	480	500	517	533	546	556	563	568	569
45°	692	716	738	757	774	788	799	807	812	814

F (x, y)

y	x									
	72°	74°	76°	78°	80°	82°	84°	86°	88°	90°
45°	.8692	.8716	.8738	.8757	.8774	.8788	.8799	.8807	.8812	.8814
46°	929	955	979	.9001	.9019	.9035	.9047	.9056	.9061	.9063
47°	.9170	.9199	.9225	249	269	286	299	309	314	316
48°	415	446	475	500	523	541	556	566	573	575
49°	664	698	729	757	781	801	817	829	836	838
50°	916	954	988	1.0018	1.0044	1.0066	1.0084	1.0097	1.0104	1.0107
51°	1.0173	1.0214	1.0251	0284	031	034	036	037	038	038
52°	043	048	052	056	059	061	063	065	066	066
53°	070	075	079	083	087	090	092	093	094	095
54°	097	102	107	111	115	118	121	123	124	124
55°	125	130	136	140	144	148	151	153	154	154
56°	153	159	165	170	174	178	181	183	185	185
57°	181	188	194	200	205	209	212	215	216	217
58°	211	218	225	231	236	241	244	247	249	249
59°	241	248	256	262	268	273	277	280	282	283
60°	271	280	288	295	301	307	311	314	316	317
61°	302	311	320	328	335	341	346	350	352	352
62°	334	344	354	362	370	377	382	386	388	389
63°	366	378	388	397	406	413	419	423	426	427
64°	400	412	423	434	443	451	457	462	465	466
65°	434	447	459	471	481	490	497	502	505	506
66°	468	483	496	509	520	530	538	544	547	549
67°	504	520	535	549	561	572	580	587	591	592
68°	541	558	574	589	603	615	625	632	636	638
69°	578	597	615	631	647	660	671	679	684	686
70°	617	637	657	675	692	707	719	728	734	735
71°	656	678	700	720	739	755	769	779	786	788
72°	696	721	744	767	788	806	821	833	840	843
73°	738	764	790	815	838	859	877	890	898	901
74°	780	809	838	866	891	915	934	950	959	962
75°	824	856	887	918	947	973	996	2.013	2.024	2.028
76°	869	903	938	972	2.005	2.035	2.060	080	093	097
77°	915	952	991	2.029	065	099	129	152	167	172
78°	962	2.003	2.045	087	129	168	202	229	247	253
79°	2.010	055	102	149	195	240	280	312	333	340
80°	059	108	160	212	265	316	363	402	427	436
81°	109	163	220	279	339	398	453	499	531	542
82°	161	220	282	348	416	484	550	606	646	660
83°	213	277	346	419	496	576	654	725	775	794
84°	267	336	412	493	581	674	768	856	923	949
85°	321	396	479	570	669	777	891	3.004	3.094	3.131
86°	376	457	548	649	761	887	3.025	170	298	355
87°	431	519	618	729	856	3.002	170	359	547	643
88°	487	582	689	811	954	122	324	571	861	4.048
89°	543	645	761	895	3.053	245	486	805	4.261	741
90°	600	708	833	979	153	370	652	4.053	743	∞

E (x, y)

y	x									
	0°	2°	4°	6°	8°	10°	12°	14°	16°	18°
0°	.0000	.0000	.0000	.0000	.0000	.0000	.0000	.0000	.0000	.0000
1°	175	175	175	175	175	175	175	175	175	175
2°	349	349	349	349	349	349	349	349	349	349
3°	524	524	524	524	524	524	524	524	524	524
4°	698	698	698	698	698	698	698	698	698	698
5°	873	873	873	873	873	873	873	873	873	873
6°	.1047	.1047	.1047	.1047	.1047	.1047	.1047	.1047	.1047	.1047
7°	222	222	222	222	222	222	222	222	222	221
8°	396	396	396	396	396	396	396	396	396	396
9°	571	571	571	571	571	571	571	570	570	570
10°	745	745	745	745	745	745	745	745	745	744
11°	920	920	920	920	920	920	919	919	919	919
12°	.2094	.2094	.2094	.2094	.2094	.2094	.2094	.2094	.2093	.2093
13°	269	269	269	269	269	268	268	268	267	267
14°	443	443	443	443	443	443	442	442	442	441
15°	618	618	618	618	617	617	617	616	616	615
16°	793	792	792	792	792	791	791	790	790	789
17°	967	967	967	967	966	966	965	965	964	963
18°	.3142	.3142	.3141	.3141	.3141	.3140	.3139	.3139	.3138	.3137
19°	316	316	316	315	315	314	314	313	312	310
20°	491	491	490	490	489	489	488	487	485	484
21°	665	665	665	664	664	663	662	661	659	658
22°	840	840	839	839	838	837	836	834	833	831
23°	.4014	.4014	.4014	.4013	.4012	.4011	.4010	.4008	.4006	.4004
24°	189	189	188	187	186	185	184	182	180	177
25°	363	363	363	362	361	359	358	356	353	351
26°	538	538	537	536	535	533	531	529	526	524
27°	712	712	712	711	709	707	705	703	700	696
28°	887	887	886	885	883	881	879	876	873	869
29°	.5061	.5061	.5060	.5059	.5057	.5055	.5053	.5049	.5046	.5042
30°	236	236	235	234	232	229	226	223	219	214
31°	411	410	409	408	406	403	400	396	392	387
32°	585	585	584	582	580	577	573	569	564	559
33°	760	759	758	756	754	751	747	742	737	731
34°	934	934	933	931	928	924	920	915	909	903
35°	.6109	.6108	.6107	.6105	.6102	.6098	.6093	.6088	.6082	.6075
36°	283	283	281	279	276	272	267	261	254	247
37°	458	457	456	453	450	445	440	433	426	418
38°	632	632	630	627	624	619	613	606	598	589
39°	807	806	804	802	797	792	786	779	770	761
40°	981	981	979	976	971	966	959	951	942	932
41°	.7156	.7155	.7153	.7150	.7145	.7139	.7132	.7123	.7114	.7103
42°	330	330	328	324	319	313	305	296	285	274
43°	505	504	502	498	493	486	478	468	457	444
44°	679	679	676	672	666	659	650	640	628	615
45°	854	853	851	846	840	832	823	812	799	785

E (x, y)

y	0°	2°	4°	6°	8°	10°	12°	14°	16°	18°
						x					
45°	.7854	.7853	.7851	.7846	.7840	.7832	.7823	.7812	.7799	.7785
46°	.8029	.8028	.8025	.8020	.8014	.8006	996	984	971	956
47°	203	202	199	194	187	179	.8168	.8156	.8142	.8126
48°	378	377	373	368	361	352	341	328	312	296
49°	552	551	548	542	535	525	513	499	483	465
50°	727	725	722	716	708	698	685	671	654	635
51°	901	900	896	890	882	871	858	842	824	805
52°	.9076	.9074	.9071	.9064	.9055	.9044	.9030	.9014	995	974
53°	250	249	245	238	229	217	202	185	.9165	.9143
54°	425	423	419	412	402	389	374	356	335	312
55°	599	598	593	586	576	562	546	527	505	481
56°	774	772	768	760	749	735	718	698	675	650
57°	948	947	942	934	922	908	890	869	845	819
58°	1.0123	1.0121	1.0116	1.0108	1.0096	1.0080	1.0062	1.0040	1.0015	987
59°	030	030	029	028	027	025	023	021	0185	1.0155
60°	047	047	046	046	044	043	041	038	035	032
61°	065	064	064	063	062	060	058	055	052	049
62°	082	082	081	080	079	077	075	072	069	066
63°	100	099	099	098	096	094	092	089	086	083
64°	117	117	116	115	114	112	109	106	103	100
65°	134	134	134	132	131	129	126	123	120	116
66°	152	152	151	150	148	146	143	140	137	133
67°	169	169	168	167	165	163	161	157	154	150
68°	187	187	186	185	183	180	178	174	171	167
69°	204	204	203	202	200	198	195	191	188	183
70°	222	221	221	219	217	215	212	208	204	200
71°	239	239	238	237	235	232	229	225	221	217
72°	257	256	255	254	252	249	246	242	238	233
73°	274	274	273	271	269	267	263	259	255	250
74°	292	291	290	289	287	284	280	276	272	267
75°	309	309	308	306	304	301	297	293	289	283
76°	326	326	325	323	321	318	315	310	305	300
77°	344	344	343	341	338	335	332	327	322	317
78°	361	361	360	358	356	353	349	344	339	333
79°	379	378	377	376	373	370	366	361	356	350
80°	396	396	395	393	390	387	383	378	373	367
81°	414	413	412	410	408	404	400	395	389	383
82°	431	431	430	428	425	421	417	412	406	400
83°	449	448	447	445	442	439	434	429	423	416
84°	466	466	464	462	459	456	451	446	440	433
85°	484	483	482	480	477	473	468	463	457	450
86°	501	501	499	497	494	490	485	480	473	466
87°	518	518	517	514	511	507	502	497	490	483
88°	536	535	534	532	529	525	520	514	507	499
89°	553	553	551	549	546	542	537	531	524	516
90°	571	570	569	566	563	559	554	548	541	533

E (x, y)

y	18°	20°	22°	24°	26°	28°	30°	32°	34°	36°
0°	.0000	.0000	.0000	.0000	.0000	.0000	.0000	.0000	.0000	.0000
1°	175	175	175	175	175	175	175	175	175	175
2°	349	349	349	349	349	349	349	349	349	349
3°	524	524	524	524	524	524	524	524	524	524
4°	698	698	698	698	698	698	698	698	698	698
5°	873	873	873	872	872	872	872	872	872	872
6°	.1047	.1047	.1047	.1047	.1047	.1047	.1047	.1047	.1047	.1047
7°	221	221	221	221	221	221	221	221	221	221
8°	396	396	396	396	395	395	395	395	395	395
9°	570	570	570	570	570	569	569	569	569	569
10°	744	744	744	744	744	743	743	743	743	742
11°	919	918	918	918	918	917	917	917	916	916
12°	.2093	.2093	.2092	.2092	.2091	.2091	.2091	.2090	.2090	.2089
13°	267	267	266	266	265	265	264	264	263	262
14°	441	441	440	439	439	438	437	437	436	435
15°	615	615	614	613	612	611	611	610	609	608
16°	789	788	788	787	786	785	784	782	781	780
17°	963	962	961	960	959	958	956	955	954	952
18°	.3137	.3136	.3134	.3133	.3132	.3130	.3129	.3127	.3126	.3124
19°	310	309	308	306	305	303	301	299	297	295
20°	484	483	481	479	477	475	473	471	469	467
21°	658	656	654	652	650	648	645	643	640	637
22°	831	829	827	825	822	819	817	814	811	808
23°	.4004	.4002	.4000	997	994	991	988	985	981	878
24°	177	175	172	.4169	.4166	.4163	.4159	.4155	.4152	.4148
25°	351	348	345	341	338	334	330	326	321	317
26°	524	520	517	513	509	505	500	496	491	486
27°	696	693	689	685	680	675	670	665	660	654
28°	869	865	861	856	851	846	840	834	828	822
29°	.5042	.5037	.5032	.5027	.5022	.5016	.5010	.5003	997	990
30°	214	209	204	198	192	186	179	172	.5164	.5157
31°	387	381	375	369	362	355	348	340	332	323
32°	559	553	547	540	532	524	516	508	499	489
33°	731	725	718	710	702	693	684	675	665	655
34°	903	896	888	880	871	862	852	842	831	820
35°	.6075	.6067	.6059	.6050	.6040	.6030	.6019	.6008	997	985
36°	247	238	229	219	209	198	186	174	.6162	.6149
37°	418	409	399	389	378	366	353	340	326	312
38°	589	580	569	558	546	533	519	505	490	475
39°	761	750	739	727	714	700	685	670	654	638
40°	932	921	908	895	881	866	851	834	817	799
41°	.7103	.7091	.7078	.7064	.7049	.7033	.7016	998	980	961
42°	274	261	247	232	216	198	180	.7161	.7142	.7122
43°	444	431	416	400	382	364	345	324	303	282
44°	615	600	584	567	549	529	508	487	465	441
45°	785	770	753	734	715	694	672	649	625	600

E (x, y)

y	x									
	18°	20°	22°	24°	26°	28°	30°	32°	34°	36°
45°	.7785	.7770	.7753	.7734	.7715	.7694	.7672	.7649	.7625	.7600
46°	956	939	921	901	881	858	835	811	785	759
47°	.8126	.8108	.8089	.8068	.8046	.8022	998	972	945	917
48°	296	277	257	235	211	186	.8160	.8132	.8104	.8074
49°	465	446	424	401	376	350	322	293	262	231
50°	635	614	591	567	541	513	483	452	420	387
51°	805	783	759	733	705	675	644	612	578	542
52°	974	951	925	898	869	838	805	770	735	697
53°	.9143	.9119	.9092	.9063	.9032	.9000	965	929	891	852
54°	312	287	258	228	196	161	.9125	.9087	.9047	.9006
55°	481	454	425	393	359	323	284	244	202	159
56°	650	622	591	557	522	483	443	401	357	312
57°	819	789	757	721	684	644	602	558	512	464
58°	987	956	922	885	846	804	760	714	665	615
59°	1.0155	1.0123	1.0087	1.0049	1.0008	964	918	870	819	766
60°	032	029	025	021	0170	1.0124	1.0076	1.0025	972	917
61°	049	046	042	038	033	028	023	0180	1.0124	1.0067
62°	066	062	058	054	049	044	039	033	028	022
63°	083	079	075	070	065	060	055	049	043	037
64°	100	096	091	086	081	076	070	064	058	051
65°	116	112	108	103	097	092	086	080	073	066
66°	133	129	124	119	113	108	101	095	088	081
67°	150	145	140	135	129	123	117	110	103	096
68°	167	162	157	151	145	139	132	125	118	110
69°	183	178	173	167	161	155	148	140	133	125
70°	200	195	189	184	177	170	163	156	148	139
71°	217	211	206	200	193	186	179	171	163	154
72°	233	228	222	216	209	202	194	186	177	168
73°	250	244	238	232	225	217	209	201	192	183
74°	267	261	255	248	241	233	225	216	207	197
75°	283	277	271	264	256	248	240	231	222	212
76°	300	294	287	280	272	264	255	246	236	226
77°	317	310	303	296	288	279	270	261	251	240
78°	333	327	320	312	304	295	286	276	265	255
79°	350	343	336	328	320	310	301	291	280	269
80°	367	360	352	344	335	326	316	306	295	283
81°	383	376	368	360	351	341	331	320	309	297
82°	400	393	385	376	367	357	346	335	324	312
83°	416	409	401	392	382	372	362	350	338	326
84°	433	425	417	408	398	388	377	365	353	340
85°	450	442	433	424	414	403	392	380	367	354
86°	466	458	449	440	430	419	407	395	382	368
87°	483	475	466	456	445	434	422	409	396	382
88°	499	491	482	472	461	449	437	424	411	397
89°	516	507	498	488	477	465	452	439	425	411
90°	533	524	514	504	492	480	467	454	440	425

E (x, y)

y	36°	38°	40°	42°	44°	46°	48°	50°	52°	54°
					x					
0°	.0000	.0000	.0000	.0000	.0000	.0000	.0000	.0000	.0000	.0000
1°	175	175	175	175	175	175	175	175	175	175
2°	349	349	349	349	349	349	349	349	349	349
3°	524	524	523	523	523	523	523	523	523	523
4°	698	698	698	698	698	698	698	698	698	698
5°	872	872	872	872	872	872	872	872	872	872
6°	.1047	.1046	.1046	.1046	.1046	.1046	.1046	.1046	.1046	.1046
7°	221	221	220	220	220	220	220	220	220	220
8°	395	395	394	394	394	394	394	394	393	393
9°	569	568	568	568	568	567	567	567	567	567
10°	742	742	742	741	741	741	740	740	740	740
11°	916	915	915	915	914	914	913	913	913	912
12°	.2089	.2089	.2088	.2088	.2087	.2087	.2086	.2085	.2085	.2084
13°	262	262	261	260	260	259	258	258	257	256
14°	435	434	433	433	432	431	430	429	428	428
15°	608	607	606	605	604	603	602	601	600	599
16°	780	779	778	776	775	774	773	771	770	769
17°	952	951	949	948	946	945	943	942	940	939
18°	.3124	.3122	.3121	.3119	.3117	.3115	.3113	.3112	.3110	.3108
19°	295	293	291	289	287	285	283	281	279	277
20°	467	464	462	459	457	455	452	450	447	445
21°	637	635	632	629	626	623	621	618	615	612
22°	808	805	802	798	795	792	789	785	782	779
23°	978	974	971	967	963	960	956	952	948	945
24°	.4148	.4144	.4139	.4135	.4131	.4127	.4123	.4118	.4114	.4110
25°	317	312	308	303	298	293	289	284	279	274
26°	486	481	475	470	465	459	454	449	443	438
27°	654	648	643	637	631	625	619	613	607	601
28°	822	816	809	803	796	789	783	776	769	763
29°	990	983	975	968	961	953	946	938	931	924
30°	.5157	.5149	.5141	.5133	.5125	.5116	.5108	.5100	.5092	.5084
31°	323	315	306	297	288	279	270	261	252	243
32°	489	480	470	460	451	441	431	421	411	401
33°	655	645	634	623	612	602	591	580	569	558
34°	820	809	797	786	774	762	750	738	726	714
35°	985	972	960	947	934	921	908	895	882	870
36°	.6149	.6135	.6122	.6108	.6094	.6080	.6066	.6051	.6037	.6024
37°	312	298	283	268	253	237	222	207	192	177
38°	475	460	444	427	411	394	378	361	345	329
39°	638	621	604	586	568	550	533	515	497	479
40°	799	781	763	744	725	706	686	667	648	629
41°	961	941	921	901	881	860	839	818	798	778
42°	.7122	.7101	.7079	.7058	.7036	.7013	991	969	947	925
43°	282	259	237	213	190	166	.7142	.7118	.7094	.7071
44°	441	417	393	368	343	318	292	266	241	216
45°	600	575	549	522	495	468	441	414	387	360

E (x, y)

y	36°	38°	40°	42°	44°	46°	48°	50°	52°	54°
					x					
45°	.7600	.7575	.7549	.7522	.7495	.7468	.7441	.7414	.7387	.7360
46°	759	732	704	676	647	618	589	560	531	502
47°	917	888	858	828	798	767	736	705	674	644
48°	.8074	.8043	.8012	980	948	915	882	849	816	784
49°	231	198	165	.8131	.8097	.8062	.8027	992	957	923
50°	387	353	317	281	245	208	171	.8134	.8097	.8060
51°	542	506	469	431	392	353	314	275	235	196
52°	697	659	620	580	539	497	456	414	373	332
53°	852	811	770	727	684	641	597	553	509	465
54°	.9006	963	919	875	829	783	737	690	644	598
55°	159	.9114	.9068	.9021	973	925	876	827	778	729
56°	312	264	216	167	.9116	.9065	.9014	962	911	859
57°	464	414	363	311	259	205	151	.9096	.9042	988
58°	615	563	510	455	400	344	287	230	173	.9116
59°	766	712	656	599	541	481	422	362	302	242
60°	917	860	801	741	680	618	556	493	430	367
61°	1.0067	1.0007	946	883	819	755	689	623	557	491
62°	022	0154	1.0090	1.0024	958	890	821	752	683	614
63°	037	030	023	0165	1.0095	1.0024	952	880	808	736
64°	051	045	038	030	023	0158	1.0083	1.0007	932	856
65°	066	059	052	044	037	029	021	0133	1.0054	975
66°	081	074	066	058	050	042	034	026	0176	1.0093
67°	096	088	080	072	064	055	047	038	030	021
68°	110	102	094	086	077	068	060	051	042	033
69°	125	117	108	099	090	081	072	063	053	044
70°	139	131	122	113	104	094	085	075	065	056
71°	154	145	136	127	117	107	097	087	077	067
72°	168	159	150	140	130	120	110	099	089	078
73°	183	173	164	153	143	133	122	111	100	089
74°	197	187	177	167	156	145	134	123	111	100
75°	212	202	191	180	169	158	146	135	123	111
76°	226	216	205	193	182	170	158	146	134	122
77°	240	230	218	207	195	183	170	158	145	133
78°	255	243	232	220	208	195	182	170	156	143
79°	269	257	245	233	220	208	194	181	168	154
80°	283	271	259	246	233	220	206	193	179	165
81°	297	285	272	259	246	232	218	204	190	175
82°	312	299	286	272	259	244	230	215	201	186
83°	326	313	299	286	271	257	242	227	211	196
84°	340	327	313	299	284	269	254	238	222	206
85°	354	340	326	312	297	281	265	249	233	217
86°	368	354	340	325	309	293	277	261	244	227
87°	382	368	353	338	322	305	289	272	255	237
88°	397	382	366	351	334	318	300	283	265	248
89°	411	395	380	364	347	330	312	294	276	258
90°	425	409	393	377	359	342	324	306	287	268

E (x, y)

y	\(x\) 54°	56°	58°	60°	62°	64°	66°	68°	70°	72°
0°	.0000	.0000	.0000	.0000	.0000	.0000	.0000	.0000	.0000	.0000
1°	175	175	175	175	175	175	175	175	175	175
2°	349	349	349	349	349	349	349	349	349	349
3°	523	523	523	523	523	523	523	523	523	523
4°	698	698	698	698	698	698	698	698	698	698
5°	872	872	872	872	872	872	872	872	872	872
6°	.1046	.1046	.1046	.1046	.1046	.1046	.1046	.1046	.1046	.1045
7°	220	220	220	219	219	219	219	219	219	219
8°	393	393	393	393	393	393	392	392	392	392
9°	567	566	566	566	566	566	566	565	565	565
10°	740	739	739	739	738	738	738	738	738	737
11°	912	912	911	911	911	910	910	910	909	909
12°	.2084	.2084	.2083	.2083	.2083	.2082	.2082	.2081	.2081	.2081
13°	256	256	255	254	254	253	253	252	252	251
14°	428	427	426	425	425	424	423	423	422	422
15°	599	598	597	596	595	594	593	592	592	591
16°	769	768	767	765	764	763	762	761	761	760
17°	939	937	936	935	933	932	931	930	929	928
18°	.3108	.3106	.3105	.3103	.3102	.3100	.3099	.3097	.3096	.3095
19°	277	275	273	271	269	267	266	264	263	262
20°	445	443	440	438	436	434	432	430	429	427
21°	612	610	607	604	602	600	597	595	593	592
22°	779	776	773	770	767	764	762	759	757	755
23°	945	941	938	935	931	928	925	923	920	918
24°	.4110	.4106	.4102	.4098	.4095	.4091	.4088	.4085	.4082	.4079
25°	274	270	266	261	257	253	249	246	243	240
26°	438	433	428	423	419	414	410	406	402	399
27°	601	595	590	584	579	574	569	565	561	557
28°	763	756	750	744	738	733	728	723	718	714
29°	924	917	910	903	897	890	885	879	874	869
30°	.5084	.5076	.5068	.5061	.5054	.5047	.5040	.5034	.5029	.5023
31°	243	234	226	218	210	202	195	188	182	176
32°	401	392	382	373	365	356	348	341	334	328
33°	558	548	538	528	518	509	501	492	485	478
34°	714	703	692	681	671	661	651	642	634	626
35°	870	857	845	833	822	811	801	791	782	773
36°	.6024	.6010	997	984	972	960	949	938	928	919
37°	177	162	.6148	.6134	.6120	.6107	.6095	.6084	.6073	.6063
38°	329	313	297	282	267	253	240	228	216	205
39°	479	462	445	429	413	398	384	370	357	346
40°	629	610	592	575	558	541	526	511	497	485
41°	778	758	738	719	701	683	666	650	636	622
42°	925	903	882	862	842	823	805	788	772	757
43°	.7071	.7048	.7025	.7003	982	962	942	924	907	891
44°	216	191	167	144	.7121	.7099	.7078	.7059	.7040	.7023
45°	360	333	307	282	258	235	212	191	171	153

E (x, y)

y	54°	56°	58°	60°	62°	64°	66°	68°	70°	72°
45°	.7360	.7333	.7307	.7282	.7258	.7235	.7212	.7191	.7171	.7153
46°	502	474	446	419	393	368	345	322	301	281
47°	644	613	584	555	528	501	475	451	429	408
48°	784	752	720	690	660	632	604	579	555	532
49°	923	888	855	822	791	761	732	704	679	655
50°	.8060	.8024	988	954	920	888	857	828	801	775
51°	196	158	.8120	.8084	.8048	.8014	981	950	921	894
52°	332	291	251	212	174	138	.8103	.8070	.8039	.8010
53°	465	422	380	339	299	260	223	188	155	125
54°	598	552	508	464	422	381	342	305	270	237
55°	729	681	634	588	543	500	458	419	382	348
56°	859	809	759	710	663	617	573	532	493	456
57°	988	935	882	831	781	733	686	642	601	563
58°	.9116	.9060	.9004	950	897	846	798	751	707	667
59°	242	183	125	.9068	.9012	959	907	858	812	769
60°	367	305	244	184	125	.9069	.9015	963	914	869
61°	491	426	362	299	237	178	121	.9066	.9015	967
62°	614	546	478	412	347	285	225	167	113	.9063
63°	736	664	593	524	456	390	327	267	210	156
64°	856	781	707	634	563	494	427	364	304	248
65°	975	897	819	743	668	596	526	460	397	338
66°	1.0093	1.0011	930	850	772	696	623	553	487	425
67°	021	0125	1.0040	956	875	795	718	645	576	510
68°	033	024	0148	1.0061	975	892	812	735	662	594
69°	044	035	026	0164	1.0075	988	904	823	747	675
70°	056	046	036	027	0173	1.0082	994	910	830	754
71°	067	057	047	037	027	0175	1.0083	995	911	832
72°	078	067	057	047	037	027	0170	1.0078	990	907
73°	089	078	067	057	046	036	026	0159	1.0067	981
74°	100	089	077	066	055	044	034	024	0143	1.0052
75°	111	099	087	076	064	053	042	032	022	012
76°	122	110	097	085	073	062	050	039	029	019
77°	133	120	107	095	082	070	058	047	036	026
78°	143	130	117	104	091	079	066	054	043	032
79°	154	140	127	113	100	087	074	062	050	038
80°	165	151	136	122	109	095	082	069	056	045
81°	175	161	146	132	117	103	089	076	063	051
82°	186	171	156	141	126	111	097	083	069	057
83°	196	180	165	150	134	119	104	090	076	062
84°	206	190	174	158	143	127	112	097	082	068
85°	217	200	184	167	151	135	119	103	088	074
86°	227	210	193	176	159	142	126	110	094	079
87°	237	220	202	185	167	150	133	117	100	085
88°	248	230	212	194	176	158	140	123	106	090
89°	258	239	221	202	184	166	147	130	112	096
90°	268	249	230	211	192	173	155	136	118	101

E (x, y)

y	72°	74°	76°	78°	80°	82°	84°	86°	88°	90°
0°	.0000	.0000	.0000	.0000	.0000	.0000	.0000	.0000	.0000	.0000
1°	175	175	175	175	175	175	175	175	175	175
2°	349	349	349	349	349	349	349	349	349	349
3°	523	523	523	523	523	523	523	523	523	523
4°	698	698	698	698	698	698	698	698	698	698
5°	872	872	872	872	872	872	872	872	872	872
6°	.1045	.1045	.1045	.1045	.1045	.1045	.1045	.1045	.1045	.1045
7°	219	219	219	219	219	219	219	219	219	219
8°	392	392	392	392	392	392	392	392	392	392
9°	565	565	565	565	565	564	564	564	564	564
10°	737	737	737	737	737	737	737	737	736	736
11°	909	909	909	909	909	908	908	908	908	908
12°	.2081	.2080	.2080	.2080	.2080	.2079	.2079	.2079	.2079	.2079
13°	251	251	251	250	250	250	250	250	250	250
14°	422	421	421	420	420	420	419	419	419	419
15°	591	590	590	589	589	589	589	588	588	588
16°	760	759	759	758	757	757	757	757	756	756
17°	928	927	926	926	925	925	924	924	924	924
18°	.3095	.3094	.3093	.3092	.3092	.3091	.3091	.3090	.3090	.3090
19°	262	260	259	258	258	257	256	256	256	256
20°	427	426	424	423	422	422	421	421	420	420
21°	592	590	589	587	586	585	585	584	584	584
22°	755	753	752	750	749	748	747	747	746	746
23°	918	916	914	912	911	909	909	908	907	907
24°	.4079	.4077	.4075	.4073	.4071	.4070	.4069	.4068	.4068	.4067
25°	240	237	234	232	230	229	228	227	226	226
26°	399	396	393	391	389	387	385	384	384	384
27°	557	553	550	548	545	543	542	541	540	540
28°	714	710	706	703	701	699	697	696	695	695
29°	869	865	861	858	855	852	851	849	848	848
30°	.5023	.5019	.5014	.5011	.5007	.5005	.5003	.5001	.5000	.5000
31°	176	171	166	162	159	156	153	152	151	150
32°	328	322	317	312	308	305	302	301	300	299
33°	478	471	466	461	456	453	450	448	447	446
34°	626	619	613	608	603	599	596	594	592	592
35°	773	766	759	753	748	743	740	738	736	736
36°	919	911	903	896	891	886	883	880	878	878
37°	.6063	.6054	.6046	.6038	.6032	.6027	.6023	.6020	.6019	.6018
38°	205	195	186	179	172	167	162	159	157	157
39°	346	335	326	317	310	304	299	296	294	293
40°	485	473	463	454	446	439	434	431	429	428
41°	622	610	598	589	580	573	568	564	561	561
42°	757	744	732	721	712	705	699	695	692	691
43°	891	877	864	852	843	835	828	824	821	820
44°	.7023	.7008	994	981	971	962	955	951	948	947
45°	153	137	.7122	.7109	.7097	.7088	.7081	.7075	.7072	.7071

E (x, y)

y	72°	74°	76°	78°	80°	82°	84°	86°	88°	90°
						x				
45°	.7153	.7137	.7122	.7109	.7097	.7088	.7081	.7075	.7072	.7071
46°	281	264	248	234	221	211	204	198	195	193
47°	408	389	372	357	344	333	324	318	315	314
48°	532	512	494	477	464	452	443	437	433	431
49°	655	633	613	596	581	569	560	553	548	547
50°	775	752	731	713	697	684	674	666	662	660
51°	894	869	847	827	811	797	786	778	773	771
52°	.8010	984	961	940	922	907	895	887	882	880
53°	125	.8097	.8072	.8050	.8031	.8015	.8002	994	988	986
54°	237	208	181	158	137	121	107	.8098	.8092	.8090
55°	348	317	288	263	242	224	210	200	194	192
56°	456	423	393	366	344	325	310	299	293	290
57°	563	527	496	467	443	423	407	396	389	387
58°	667	630	596	566	540	519	502	490	483	480
59°	769	730	694	662	635	613	595	582	574	572
60°	869	827	790	756	728	704	685	671	663	660
61°	967	923	883	848	817	792	772	758	749	746
62°	.9063	.9016	974	937	905	878	857	842	833	829
63°	156	108	.9063	.9024	990	962	939	923	913	910
64°	248	197	150	108	.9072	.9042	.9019	.9002	991	988
65°	338	283	234	190	152	121	096	078	.9067	.9063
66°	425	368	316	270	230	196	170	151	139	135
67°	510	450	396	347	305	269	242	221	209	205
68°	594	531	473	422	377	340	310	289	276	272
69°	675	609	548	494	447	408	377	354	340	336
70°	754	685	621	564	514	473	440	416	402	397
71°	832	758	691	631	579	536	501	476	460	455
72°	907	830	760	697	642	596	559	532	516	511
73°	981	900	826	760	702	653	614	586	569	563
74°	1.0052	968	890	820	759	708	667	637	619	613
75°	0122	1.0033	952	878	814	760	717	685	666	659
76°	019	0097	1.0012	934	867	809	764	730	710	703
77°	026	016	0069	988	917	857	808	773	751	744
78°	032	022	0125	1.0040	965	901	850	812	789	781
79°	038	028	018	0090	1.0011	943	889	849	825	816
80°	045	034	023	014	0054	983	926	883	857	848
81°	051	039	028	018	0096	1.0021	959	914	886	877
82°	057	044	033	023	014	0056	991	943	913	903
83°	062	050	038	027	017	0089	1.0020	968	936	925
84°	068	055	043	031	021	012	0047	992	957	945
85°	074	060	047	035	024	015	0072	1.0012	975	962
86°	079	065	052	039	028	018	009	0031	990	976
87°	085	070	056	043	031	020	012	0047	1.0002	986
88°	090	075	060	046	034	023	014	006	0012	994
89°	096	080	064	050	037	025	015	007	0020	998
90°	101	084	069	054	040	028	017	009	0026	1.0000

H

MISCELLANEOUS TRANSCENDENTAL FUNCTIONS

Formulas

A. Error function

1. Definition

$$\operatorname{erf} x = \frac{2}{\sqrt{\pi}} \int_0^x \exp\left(-s^2\right) ds = \frac{1}{\sqrt{\pi}} \int_0^{x^2} \frac{\exp\left(-s\right)}{\sqrt{s}} ds$$

2. Power series

$$\operatorname{erf} x = \frac{2}{\sqrt{\pi}} \left(x - \frac{x^3}{3 \cdot 1!} + \frac{x^5}{5 \cdot 2!} - \frac{x^7}{7 \cdot 3!} + - \cdots \right)$$

3. Asymptotic expansion

$$\operatorname{erf} x \approx 1 - \frac{\exp\left(-x^2\right)}{\sqrt{\pi} x} \left(1 - \frac{1}{2 x^2} + \frac{1 \cdot 3}{2^2 x^4} - \frac{1 \cdot 3 \cdot 5}{2^3 x^6} + - \cdots \right)$$

4. Integrals leading to the error function

$$\int_0^x \exp\left(-a^2 s^2\right) ds = \frac{\sqrt{\pi}}{2 a} \operatorname{erf}\left(a x\right)$$

$$\int_0^x \exp\left(-s\right) \sqrt{s}\, ds = \frac{\sqrt{\pi}}{2} \operatorname{erf}\left(\sqrt{x}\right) - \sqrt{x}\, e^{-x}$$

$$\int_0^x \exp\left(-\frac{1}{s}\right) \frac{ds}{\sqrt{s}} = 2 \sqrt{x}\, e^{-1/x} - 2 \sqrt{\pi} \left[1 - \operatorname{erf}\left(1/\sqrt{x}\right) \right]$$

$$\int_0^x \exp\left(-\frac{1}{s}\right) \frac{ds}{s \sqrt{s}} = \sqrt{\pi} \left[1 - \operatorname{erf}\left(1/\sqrt{x}\right) \right]$$

5. Derivative

$$\frac{d}{dx} \operatorname{erf}(ax) = \frac{2\,a}{\sqrt{\pi}} \exp(-a^2x^2)$$

6. Integrals

$$\int_0^x \operatorname{erf}(\sqrt{s})\,ds = (x - \tfrac{1}{2})\operatorname{erf}(\sqrt{x}) + \sqrt{\frac{x}{\pi}}\,e^{-x}$$

$$\int_0^x \operatorname{erf}(\sqrt{s})\,s\,ds = \tfrac{1}{2}(x^2 - \tfrac{3}{4})\operatorname{erf}(\sqrt{x}) + \tfrac{1}{2}(x + \tfrac{3}{2})\sqrt{\frac{x}{\pi}}\,e^{-x}$$

7. Extreme values of the argument x

For very small arguments use the power series (2); for $x > 3$ use the asymptotic expansion (3).

8. Bibliography

J. BURGESS: *Trans. Roy Soc. Edinburgh*, vol. 39, II (1898), pp. 283–320.

erf x with   9 dec. for $x = 0.000\,(0.001)\,1.249$,

" 15 " " $x = 1.000\,(0.001)\,1.500$,

" 15 " " $x = 1.500\,(0.002)\,3.000$.

Author's notation: H (t) for erf t.

B. Fresnel's Integrals

1. *Definition*

$$C(x) = \frac{1}{\sqrt{2\pi}} \int_0^x \frac{\cos s}{\sqrt{s}}\, ds \qquad\qquad S(x) = \frac{1}{\sqrt{2\pi}} \int_0^x \frac{\sin s}{\sqrt{s}}\, ds$$

2. *Series representations*

$$C(x) = \sqrt{\frac{2x}{\pi}} \left[1 - \frac{x^2}{5 \cdot 2!} + \frac{x^4}{9 \cdot 4!} - \frac{x^6}{13 \cdot 6!} + - \ldots \right]$$

$$S(x) = \sqrt{\frac{2x}{\pi}} \left[\frac{x}{3 \cdot 1!} - \frac{x^3}{7 \cdot 3!} + \frac{x^5}{11 \cdot 5!} - \frac{x^7}{15 \cdot 7!} + - \ldots \right]$$

$$C(x) = \sqrt{\frac{2x}{\pi}} \left[\left(1 - \frac{(2x)^2}{1 \cdot 3 \cdot 5} + \frac{(2x)^4}{1 \cdot 3 \cdot 5 \cdot 7 \cdot 9} - \right.\right.$$

$$\left. - \frac{(2x)^6}{1 \cdot 3 \cdot 5 \cdot 7 \cdot 9 \cdot 11 \cdot 13} + - \ldots \right) \cos x +$$

$$\left. + \left(\frac{2x}{1 \cdot 3} - \frac{(2x)^3}{1 \cdot 3 \cdot 5 \cdot 7} + \frac{(2x)^5}{1 \cdot 3 \cdot 5 \cdot 7 \cdot 9 \cdot 11} - + \ldots \right) \sin x \right]$$

$$S(x) = \sqrt{\frac{2x}{\pi}} \left[\left(1 - \frac{(2x)^2}{1 \cdot 3 \cdot 5} + \frac{(2x)^4}{1 \cdot 3 \cdot 5 \cdot 7 \cdot 9} - \right.\right.$$

$$\left. - \frac{(2x)^6}{1 \cdot 3 \cdot 5 \cdot 7 \cdot 9 \cdot 11 \cdot 13} + - \ldots \right) \sin x -$$

$$\left. - \left(\frac{2x}{1 \cdot 3} - \frac{(2x)^3}{1 \cdot 3 \cdot 5 \cdot 7} + \frac{(2x)^5}{1 \cdot 3 \cdot 5 \cdot 7 \cdot 9 \cdot 11} - + \ldots \right) \cos x \right]$$

3. *Asymptotic expansions*

See the general remark on asymptotic expansions on p. 39.

$$C(x) \approx \tfrac{1}{2} + \frac{1}{\sqrt{2\pi x}}\left[\left(1 - \frac{1\cdot 3}{(2x)^2} + \frac{1\cdot 3\cdot 5\cdot 7}{(2x)^4}\right.\right.$$

$$\left. - \frac{1\cdot 3\cdot 5\cdot 7\cdot 9\cdot 11}{(2x)^6} + - \ldots\right)\sin x -$$

$$\left. - \left(\frac{1}{2x} - \frac{1\cdot 3\cdot 5}{(2x)^3} + \frac{1\cdot 3\cdot 5\cdot 7\cdot 9}{(2x)^5} - + \ldots\right)\cos x\right]$$

$$S(x) \approx \tfrac{1}{2} - \frac{1}{\sqrt{2\pi x}}\left[\left(1 - \frac{1\cdot 3}{(2x)^2} + \frac{1\cdot 3\cdot 5\cdot 7}{(2x)^4}\right.\right.$$

$$\left. - \frac{1\cdot 3\cdot 5\cdot 7\cdot 9\cdot 11}{(2x)^6} + - \ldots\right)\cos x +$$

$$\left. + \left(\frac{1}{2x} - \frac{1\cdot 3\cdot 5}{(2x)^3} + \frac{1\cdot 3\cdot 5\cdot 7\cdot 9}{(2x)^5} - + \ldots\right)\sin x\right]$$

4. *Integrals leading to Fresnel's integrals*

$$\int_0^x \cos\frac{\pi s^2}{2}\,ds = C\left(\frac{\pi x^2}{2}\right) \qquad \int_0^x \sin\frac{\pi s^2}{2}\,ds = S\left(\frac{\pi x^2}{2}\right)$$

$$\int_0^\infty \frac{e^{-xs}}{1 + s^2}\frac{ds}{\sqrt{s}} = \frac{\pi}{\sqrt{2}}\left[2\,C(x)\sin x - 2\,S(x)\cos x + \cos x - \sin x\right]$$

$$\int_0^\infty \frac{e^{-xs}}{1 + s^2}\sqrt{s}\,ds = -\frac{\pi}{\sqrt{2}}\left[2\,C(x)\cos x + 2\,S(x)\sin x - \cos x - \sin x\right]$$

5. *Derivatives*

$$\frac{d}{dx}\,C(x) = \frac{\cos x}{\sqrt{2\pi x}} \qquad\qquad \frac{d}{dx}\,S(x) = \frac{\sin x}{\sqrt{2\pi x}}$$

6.   Integrals

$$\int_0^x C(s)\, ds = x\, C(x) + \tfrac{1}{2} S(x) - \sqrt{\frac{x}{2\pi}}\, \sin x$$

$$\int_0^x S(s)\, ds = x\, S(x) - \tfrac{1}{2} C(x) + \sqrt{\frac{x}{2\pi}}\, \cos x$$

$$\int_0^x C(s^2)\, ds = x\, C(x^2) - \frac{1}{\sqrt{2\pi}}\, \sin (x^2)$$

$$\int_0^x S(s^2)\, ds = x\, S(x^2) - \frac{1}{\sqrt{2\pi}}\, (1 - \cos (x^2))$$

7.   Extreme values of the argument x

For very small arguments use the power series (2); for $x > 10$ use the asymptotic expansions (3).

8.   Bibliography

E. LOMMEL: *Abh. math.-phys. Classe, Bayer. Akad. Wiss., München,* vol. 15, (1886), pp. 648–650.
C (x), S (x) with 6 dig. for $x = 0.0\,(0.1)\,1.0$,
$$x = 1.0\,(0.5)\,50.0$$
and interpolation coefficients.

Author's notation:

$$\tfrac{1}{2} \int_0^z I_{-1/2}\, dz \quad \text{and} \quad \tfrac{1}{2} \int_0^z I_{1/2}\, dz \text{ for C } (z) \text{ and S } (z).$$

C. Sine integral, cosine integral, exponential integral

1. Definitions

Cosine integral:

$$\mathrm{Ci}\ x = -\int_{x}^{\infty} \frac{\cos s}{s}\, ds$$

sine integral:

$$\mathrm{Si}\ x = \int_{0}^{x} \frac{\sin s}{s}\, ds$$

exponential integral:

$$\mathrm{Ei}\ x = \int_{-\infty}^{x} \frac{e^{s}}{s}\, ds.$$

Since the integrand has a singularity at $s = 0$, this formula defines the real function Ei x only for $x < 0$. In the complex plane the exponential integral is multivalued and assumes complex values on the positive real axis:

$$\mathrm{Ei}\ x = \overline{\mathrm{Ei}}\ x + n\, i\, \pi,$$

where $n = \pm\, 1, \pm\, 3, \pm\, 5, \ldots$, and $\overline{\mathrm{Ei}}\ x$ has real values for real $x > 0$. In particular one has

$$\mathrm{Ei}\ (x + i\, 0) = \overline{\mathrm{Ei}}\ x - i\, \pi,$$
$$\mathrm{Ei}\ (x - i\, 0) = \overline{\mathrm{Ei}}\ x + i\, \pi.$$

2. Power series

$$\mathrm{Ci}\ x = \ln \gamma x - \frac{x^{2}}{2 \cdot 2!} + \frac{x^{4}}{4 \cdot 4!} - + \ldots$$

$$\mathrm{Si}\ x = x - \frac{x^{3}}{3 \cdot 3!} + \frac{x^{5}}{5 \cdot 5!} - \frac{x^{7}}{7 \cdot 7!} + - \ldots$$

$$\mathrm{Ei}\ (- x) = \ln \gamma x - \frac{x}{1 \cdot 1!} + \frac{x^{2}}{2 \cdot 2!} - \frac{x^{3}}{3 \cdot 3!} + - \ldots$$

$$\overline{\mathrm{Ei}}\ x = \ln \gamma x + \frac{x}{1 \cdot 1!} + \frac{x^{2}}{2 \cdot 2!} + \frac{x^{3}}{3 \cdot 3!} + \ldots$$

3. *Asymptotic expansions*

See the remark on asymptotic expansions on p. 39.

$$\text{Ci } x \approx - \left(\frac{1!}{x^2} - \frac{3!}{x^4} + \frac{5!}{x^6} - + \dots \right) \cos x$$

$$+ \left(\frac{0!}{x} - \frac{2!}{x^3} + \frac{4!}{x^5} - + \dots \right) \sin x$$

$$\text{Si } x \approx \frac{\pi}{2} - \left(\frac{1!}{x^2} - \frac{3!}{x^4} + \frac{5!}{x^6} - + \dots \right) \sin x$$

$$- \left(\frac{0!}{x} - \frac{2!}{x^3} + \frac{4!}{x^5} - + \dots \right) \cos x$$

$$\text{Ei } (-x) \approx - e^{-x} \left(\frac{0!}{x} - \frac{1!}{x^2} + \frac{2!}{x^3} - + \dots \right)$$

$$\overline{\text{Ei}} \, x \approx e^x \left(\frac{0!}{x} + \frac{1!}{x^2} + \frac{2!}{x^3} + \dots \right)$$

4. *Extreme values of the argument x*

For very small arguments use the power series (2); for $x > 10$ use the asymptotic expansions (3).

5. *Bibliography*

Mathematical Tables Project: *Tables of Sine, Cosine and Exponential Integrals.* Vols. 1, 2. 1940.

Vol. 1:
Ci x, Si x, $\overline{\text{Ei}}$ x, Ei $(-x)$ with 9 dec. for $x = 0.0000\ (0.0001)\ 1.9999$.

Vol. 2:
Ci x, Si x with 10 dec. for $x = 0.000\ (0.001)\ 9.999$,
$\overline{\text{Ei}}$ x ,, 10 dig. ,, $x = 0.000\ (0.001)\ 9.999$,
Ei $(-x)$,, 9 ,,   ,, $x = 0.000\ (0.001)\ 9.999$.

Author's notation: Ei (x) for $\overline{\text{Ei}}$ x.

Mathematical Tables Project: *Table of Sine and Cosine Integrals.* 1942.
Ci x, Si x with 10 dec. for $x = 10.00\ (0.01)\ 100.00$.

D. Factorial function and gamma function

1. Definition

Factorial function:

$$\ln (x!) = \sum_{n=1}^{\infty} \left[x \ln \left(1 + \frac{1}{n} \right) - \ln \left(1 + \frac{x}{n} \right) \right]$$

$$x! = \prod_{n=1}^{\infty} \frac{\left(1 + \frac{1}{n} \right)^x}{1 + \frac{x}{n}}$$

For positive integers x this definition is identical with

$$x! = 1 \cdot 2 \cdot 3 \cdot 4 \cdot \ldots \cdot (x - 1) \cdot x.$$

Gamma function:

$$\Gamma (x) = (x - 1)!, \quad x! = \Gamma (x + 1)$$

2. Relations between functions of different arguments

$$x! = x \cdot (x - 1)! \qquad \Gamma (x) = (x - 1) \cdot \Gamma (x - 1)$$

$$(- x)! = \frac{\pi x}{x! \sin \pi x} \qquad \Gamma (- x) = - \frac{\pi}{\Gamma (x + 1) \sin \pi x}$$

$$x! \cdot (x - \tfrac{1}{2})! = \frac{\sqrt{\pi} \cdot (2x)!}{4^x} = \Gamma (x + 1) \cdot \Gamma (x + \tfrac{1}{2})$$

3. Special values

$$\tfrac{1}{2}! = \Gamma (\tfrac{3}{2}) = \tfrac{1}{2} \sqrt{\pi}, \qquad (- \tfrac{1}{2})! = \Gamma (\tfrac{1}{2}) = \sqrt{\pi}$$

minimum: $0.4616! = \Gamma (1.4616) = 0.8856$

4. Integrals

$$\int_0^{\infty} e^{-s} s^x \, ds = x!, \qquad x > - 1$$

4. *continued*

$$\int_0^\infty e^{-a^2 s^2} s^x \, ds = \frac{\sqrt{\pi} \, x!}{(2a)^{x+1} \cdot (x/2)!}, \qquad x > -1, \qquad a \neq 0$$

$$\int_0^1 s^x (1 - s)^y \, ds = \frac{x! \, y!}{(1 + x + y)!}, \qquad x > -1, \qquad y > -1$$

$$\int_0^\infty s^x (1 + s)^{-y} \, ds = \frac{x! \, (y - x - 2)!}{(y - 1)!}, \qquad x > -1, \qquad y > 0$$

$$\int_0^1 \frac{ds}{\sqrt{1 - s^n}} = \frac{4^{1/n} \cdot (1/n)!^2}{(2/n)!}$$

5. *Arguments x beyond the range of the table*

Use the formulas (2) to obtain an argument within that range.

6. *Bibliography*

G. Cassinis: *Ist. Naz. Assicurazioni, Roma, Atti*, vol. 2 (1930), p. 257–263.
$\Gamma(x)$ with 7 dec. for $x = 1.000 \, (0.001) \, 2.050$.

H. T. Davis: *Tables of the Higher Mathematical Functions*, vol. 1.   Bloomington, Ind., 1933, pp. 196–268.
$\Gamma(x)$ with 10 dec. for $x = 1.0000 \, (0.0001) \, 1.1000$,
      ,, 10 ,, ,, $x = 1.000 \, (0.001) \, 2.000$,
$\Gamma(-x)$,, 10 dig. ,, $x = 0.01 \, (0.01) \, 10.00$.

British Association for the Advancement of Science: *Mathematical Tables*, Vol. 1.   Cambridge, 1946, p. 40.
$x!$ with 10 dec. for $x = 0.00 \, (0.01) \, 1.00$.

erf x

x	0	1	2	3	4	5	6	7	8	9
0.00	.00000	113	226	339	451	564	677	790	903	*016
1	1128	241	354	467	580	692	805	918	*031	*144
2	2256	369	482	595	708	820	933	*046	*159	*271
3	3384	497	610	722	835	948	*060	*173	*286	*398
4	4511	624	736	849	962	*074	*187	*299	*412	*525
5	5637	750	862	975	*087	*200	*312	*425	*537	*650
6	6762	875	987	*099	*212	*324	*437	*549	*661	*773
7	7886	998	*110	*223	*335	*447	*559	*671	*784	*896
8	9008	120	232	344	456	568	680	792	904	*016
9	.1013	024	035	046	058	069	080	091	102	113
.10	125	136	147	158	169	180	192	203	214	225
1	236	247	259	270	281	292	303	314	325	336
2	348	359	370	381	392	403	414	425	436	448
3	459	470	481	492	503	514	525	536	547	558
4	569	581	592	603	614	625	636	647	658	669
5	680	691	702	713	724	735	746	757	768	779
6	790	801	812	823	834	845	856	867	878	889
7	900	911	922	933	944	955	966	977	988	998
8	.2009	020	031	042	053	064	075	086	097	108
9	118	129	140	151	162	173	184	194	205	216
.20	227	238	249	260	270	281	292	303	314	324
1	335	346	357	368	378	389	400	411	421	432
2	443	454	464	475	486	497	507	518	529	540
3	550	561	572	582	593	604	614	625	636	646
4	657	668	678	689	700	710	721	731	742	753
5	763	774	784	795	806	816	827	837	848	858
6	869	880	890	901	911	922	932	943	953	964
7	974	985	995	*006	*016	*027	*037	*047	*058	*068
8	.3079	089	100	110	120	131	141	152	162	172
9	183	193	204	214	224	235	245	255	266	276
.30	286	297	307	317	327	338	348	358	369	379
1	389	399	410	420	430	440	450	461	471	481
2	491	501	512	522	532	542	552	562	573	583
3	593	603	613	623	633	643	653	663	674	684
4	694	704	714	724	734	744	754	764	774	784
5	794	804	814	824	834	844	854	864	873	883
6	893	903	913	923	933	943	953	963	972	982
7	992	*002	*012	*022	*031	*041	*051	*061	*071	*080
8	.4090	100	110	119	129	139	149	158	168	178
9	187	197	207	216	226	236	245	255	265	274
.40	284	294	303	313	322	332	341	351	361	370
1	380	389	399	408	418	427	437	446	456	465
2	475	484	494	503	512	522	531	541	550	359
3	569	578	588	597	606	616	625	634	644	653
4	662	672	681	690	699	709	718	727	736	746
5	755	764	773	782	792	801	810	819	828	837
6	847	856	865	874	883	892	901	910	919	928
7	937	946	956	965	974	983	992	*001	*010	*019
8	.5027	036	045	054	063	072	081	090	099	108
9	117	126	134	143	152	161	170	179	187	196
.50	205	214	223	231	240	249	258	266	275	284

MISCELLANEOUS TRANSCENDENTAL FUNCTIONS

erf x

x	0	1	2	3	4	5	6	7	8	9
.50	.5205	214	223	231	240	249	258	266	275	284
1	292	301	310	318	327	336	344	353	362	370
2	379	388	396	405	413	422	430	439	448	456
3	465	473	482	490	499	507	516	524	533	541
4	549	558	566	575	583	591	600	608	617	625
5	633	642	650	658	667	675	683	691	700	708
6	716	724	733	741	749	757	765	774	782	790
7	798	806	814	823	831	839	847	855	863	871
8	879	887	895	903	911	919	927	935	943	951
9	959	967	975	983	991	999	*007	*015	*023	*031
.60	.6039	046	054	062	070	078	086	093	101	109
1	117	125	132	140	148	156	163	171	179	186
2	194	202	209	217	225	232	240	248	255	263
3	270	278	286	293	301	308	316	323	331	338
4	346	353	361	368	376	383	391	398	405	413
5	420	428	435	442	450	457	464	472	479	486
6	494	501	508	516	523	530	537	545	552	559
7	566	573	581	588	595	602	609	616	624	631
8	638	645	652	659	666	673	680	687	694	701
9	708	715	722	729	736	743	750	757	764	771
.70	778	785	792	799	806	812	819	826	833	840
1	847	853	860	867	874	881	887	894	901	908
2	914	921	928	934	941	948	954	961	968	974
3	981	988	994	*001	*007	*014	*021	*027	*034	*040
4	.7047	053	060	066	073	079	086	092	099	105
5	112	118	124	131	137	144	150	156	163	169
6	175	182	188	194	201	207	213	219	226	232
7	238	244	251	257	263	269	275	282	288	294
8	300	306	312	318	325	331	337	343	349	355
9	361	367	373	379	385	391	397	403	409	415
.80	421	427	433	439	445	451	457	462	468	474
1	480	486	492	498	503	509	515	521	527	532
2	538	544	550	555	561	567	572	578	584	590
3	595	601	607	612	618	623	629	635	640	646
4	651	657	663	668	674	679	685	690	696	701
5	707	712	718	723	729	734	739	745	750	756
6	761	766	772	777	782	788	793	798	804	809
7	814	820	825	830	835	841	846	851	856	862
8	867	872	877	882	888	893	898	903	908	913
9	918	924	929	934	939	944	949	954	959	964
.90	969	974	979	984	989	994	999	*004	*009	*014
1	.8019	024	029	034	038	043	048	053	058	063
2	068	073	077	082	087	092	097	101	106	111
3	116	120	125	130	135	139	144	149	153	158
4	163	167	172	177	181	186	191	195	200	204
5	209	213	218	223	227	232	236	241	245	250
6	254	259	263	268	272	277	281	285	290	294
7	299	303	307	312	316	321	325	329	334	338
8	342	347	351	355	360	364	368	372	377	381
9	385	389	394	398	402	406	410	415	419	423
1.00	427	431	435	439	444	448	452	456	460	464

$1 - \text{erf } x$

x	0	1	2	3	4	5	6	7	8	9
1.0	0.1573	532	492	452	414	376	339	302	267	232
1	198	165	132	100	069	039	009	*9800	*9516	*9239
2	$10^{-1} \times 0.8969$	8704	8447	8195	7949	7710	7476	7249	7027	6810
3	6599	6394	6193	5998	5809	5624	5444	5269	5098	4933
4	4771	4615	4462	4314	4170	4030	3895	3763	3635	3510
5	3389	3272	3159	3048	2941	2838	2737	2640	2545	2454
6	2365	2279	2196	2116	2038	1962	1890	1819	1751	1685
7	1621	1559	1500	1442	1387	1333	1281	1231	1183	1136
8	1091	1048	1006	09653	09264	08889	08528	08179	07844	07521
9	$10^{-2} \times 0.7210$	6910	6622	6344	6077	5821	5574	5336	5108	4889
2.0	4678	4475	4281	4094	3914	3742	3577	3418	3266	3120
1	2979	2845	2716	2593	2475	2361	2253	2149	2049	1954
2	1863	1776	1692	1612	1536	1463	1393	1326	1262	1201
3	1143	1088	1034	09838	09354	08893	08452	08032	07631	07249
4	$10^{-3} \times 0.6885$	6538	6207	5892	5592	5306	5034	4774	4528	4293
5	4070	3857	3655	3463	3280	3107	2942	2785	2636	2495
6	2360	2233	2112	1997	1888	1785	1687	1594	1506	1422
7	1343	1268	1197	1130	1066	1006	09492	08952	08441	07958
8	$10^{-4} \times 0.7501$	7069	6661	6275	5910	5566	5240	4933	4642	4368
9	4110	3866	3635	3418	3213	3020	2838	2667	2505	2353
3.0	2209	2074	1947	1827	1714	1608	1508	1414	1326	1243

C (x)

x	0	1	2	3	4	5	6	7	8	9
0.0	.0000	0798	1128	1382	1596	1784	1954	2110	2255	2392
1	.2521	2643	2760	2872	2980	3083	3183	3280	3374	3465
2	.3554	3640	3724	3806	3886	3965	4041	4116	4189	4261
3	.4331	4400	4468	4534	4599	4663	4726	4787	4848	4908
4	.4966	5024	5080	5136	5191	5245	5298	5350	5402	5453
5	.5502	5552	5600	5648	5695	5741	5786	5831	5875	5919
6	.5962	6004	6045	6086	6127	6166	6205	6244	6282	6319
7	.6356	392	428	463	497	531	565	598	630	662
8	693	724	754	784	813	842	870	898	926	952
9	979	*005	*030	*055	*080	*104	*127	*150	*173	*195
1.0	.7217	238	259	280	300	319	339	357	376	393
1	411	428	445	461	476	492	507	522	536	550
2	563	576	589	601	613	624	635	646	656	666
3	676	685	694	702	710	718	725	732	739	745
4	751	756	762	766	771	775	779	782	786	788
5	791	793	795	796	797	798	799	799	799	798
6	798	796	795	793	791	789	787	784	780	777
7	773	769	765	760	755	750	744	738	732	726
8	719	713	705	698	690	682	674	666	657	648
9	639	629	619	610	599	589	578	567	556	545
2.0	533	521	509	497	484	472	459	445	432	418
1	405	391	376	362	347	333	318	302	287	272
2	256	240	224	208	191	174	158	141	124	106
3	089	071	053	036	017	*999	*981	*962	*944	*925
4	.6906	887	868	849	829	809	790	770	750	730
5	710	690	669	649	628	607	587	566	545	524
6	503	481	460	439	417	396	374	352	330	309
7	287	265	243	221	198	176	154	132	109	087
8	064	042	019	*997	*974	*952	*929	*906	*884	*861
9	.5838	815	793	770	747	724	701	679	656	633
3.0	610	587	565	542	519	496	474	451	428	405
1	383	360	338	315	292	270	248	225	203	180
2	158	136	114	092	069	047	025	004	*982	*960
3	.4938	917	895	873	852	831	809	788	767	746
4	725	704	683	663	642	622	601	581	561	540
5	520	501	481	461	441	422	403	383	364	345
6	326	307	289	270	252	233	215	197	179	162
7	144	126	109	092	075	058	041	024	008	*991
8	.3975	959	943	927	911	896	880	865	850	835
9	821	806	792	777	763	749	735	722	708	695
4.0	682	669	656	644	631	619	607	595	583	571
1	560	549	538	527	516	506	495	485	475	465
2	456	446	437	428	419	410	402	393	385	377
3	369	362	354	347	340	333	326	320	314	308
4	302	296	290	285	280	275	270	265	261	257
5	252	249	245	241	238	235	232	229	227	224
6	222	220	218	217	215	214	213	212	212	211
7	211	211	211	211	211	212	213	214	215	216
8	218	219	221	223	225	228	230	233	236	239
9	242	246	249	253	257	261	266	270	275	280
5.0	285	290	295	300	306	312	318	324	331	337

S (x)

x	0	1	2	3	4	5	6	7	8	9
0.0	.0000	003	008	014	021	030	039	049	060	072
1	084	097	110	125	139	154	170	186	203	220
2	237	255	273	292	311	331	351	371	392	413
3	434	456	478	500	523	546	569	593	617	641
4	665	690	715	740	766	791	817	844	870	897
5	924	951	978	*006	*034	*062	*090	*118	*147	*176
6	.1205	234	263	293	322	352	382	412	443	473
7	504	535	566	597	628	659	691	722	754	786
8	818	850	882	914	947	979	*012	*044	*077	*110
9	.2143	176	209	242	275	308	342	375	409	442
1.0	476	509	543	576	610	644	678	712	745	779
1	813	847	881	915	949	983	*017	*051	*085	*119
2	.3153	187	220	254	288	322	356	390	424	457
3	491	525	558	592	626	659	693	726	759	793
4	826	859	892	925	958	991	*024	*057	*090	*122
5	.4155	187	220	252	284	316	348	380	412	444
6	475	507	538	569	600	631	662	693	724	754
7	785	815	845	875	905	935	964	994	*023	*052
8	.5081	110	139	167	196	224	252	280	308	336
9	363	390	418	445	471	498	524	551	577	603
2.0	628	654	679	705	730	754	779	804	828	852
1	876	899	923	946	969	992	*015	*037	*059	*081
2	.6103	125	146	168	189	209	230	250	271	291
3	310	330	349	368	387	406	424	442	460	478
4	495	513	530	546	563	579	596	612	627	643
5	658	673	688	702	716	730	744	758	771	784
6	797	810	822	834	846	858	869	881	892	902
7	913	923	933	943	952	962	971	980	988	997
8	.7005	013	020	028	035	042	048	055	061	067
9	073	078	083	088	093	098	102	106	110	113
3.0	117	120	123	126	128	130	132	134	135	137
1	138	139	139	140	140	140	139	139	138	137
2	136	134	133	131	129	127	124	121	118	115
3	112	108	105	101	096	092	087	083	078	072
4	067	061	055	049	043	037	030	023	016	009
5	002	*994	*986	*978	*970	*962	*954	*945	*936	*927
6	.6918	908	899	889	879	869	859	848	838	827
7	816	805	794	782	771	759	747	735	723	711
8	698	686	673	660	647	634	621	607	594	580
9	566	552	538	524	510	495	481	466	451	436
4.0	421	406	391	376	360	344	329	313	297	281
1	265	249	233	216	200	183	167	150	133	116
2	099	082	065	048	031	014	*996	*979	*961	*944
3	.5926	909	891	873	855	837	820	802	784	766
4	747	729	711	693	675	657	638	620	602	583
5	565	547	528	510	491	473	454	436	417	399
6	380	362	343	325	306	288	270	251	233	214
7	196	177	159	141	122	104	086	068	049	031
8	013	*995	*977	*959	*941	*923	*905	*887	*869	*851
9	.4834	816	798	781	763	746	728	711	694	677
5.0	659	642	625	608	592	575	558	541	525	508

C (x)

x	0	1	2	3	4	5	6	7	8	9
5.0	.3285	290	295	300	306	312	318	324	331	337
1	343	350	357	364	371	379	386	394	402	410
2	418	426	434	443	452	461	470	479	488	497
3	507	517	526	536	546	557	567	577	588	599
4	610	620	632	643	654	666	677	689	701	712
5	724	737	749	761	773	786	799	811	824	837
6	850	863	876	890	903	917	930	944	958	971
7	985	999	*013	*028	*042	*056	*070	*085	*099	*114
8	.4129	143	158	173	188	203	218	233	248	263
9	278	294	309	324	340	355	370	386	402	417
6.0	433	448	464	480	496	511	527	543	559	575
1	590	606	622	638	654	670	686	702	718	734
2	750	766	782	798	814	830	846	862	877	893
3	909	925	941	957	973	988	*004	*020	*036	*052
4	.5067	083	098	114	130	145	161	176	191	207
5	222	237	252	268	283	298	313	328	343	358
6	372	387	402	416	431	445	460	474	488	503
7	517	531	545	559	572	586	600	613	627	640
8	654	667	680	692	706	719	732	745	757	770
9	782	795	807	819	831	843	855	867	878	890
7.0	901	912	924	935	946	957	967	978	989	999
1	.6009	020	030	040	049	059	069	078	088	097
2	106	115	124	132	141	150	158	166	174	182
3	190	198	205	213	220	227	234	241	248	255
4	261	267	274	280	286	291	297	303	308	313
5	318	323	328	333	338	342	346	350	354	358
6	362	365	369	372	375	378	381	384	386	389
7	391	393	395	397	399	400	402	403	404	405
8	406	407	407	408	408	408	408	408	408	407
9	407	406	405	404	403	402	400	399	397	395
8.0	393	391	389	386	384	381	378	375	372	369
1	366	362	359	355	351	347	343	339	334	330
2	325	320	315	310	305	300	294	289	283	277
3	271	265	259	253	246	240	233	227	220	213
4	206	198	191	184	176	169	161	153	145	137
5	129	120	112	104	095	086	077	069	060	050
6	041	032	023	013	004	*994	*984	*974	*964	*954
7	.5944	934	924	914	903	893	882	871	861	850
8	839	828	817	806	795	784	772	761	750	738
9	727	715	703	692	680	668	656	644	632	620
9.0	608	596	584	571	559	547	535	522	510	497
1	485	472	460	447	434	422	409	396	383	371
2	358	345	332	319	306	293	281	268	255	242
3	229	216	203	190	177	164	151	138	125	112
4	099	086	073	060	047	034	021	008	*995	*982
5	.4969	956	943	930	917	905	892	879	866	854
6	841	828	816	803	790	778	765	753	741	728
7	716	703	691	679	667	655	643	631	619	607
8	595	583	571	559	548	536	525	513	502	490
9	479	468	457	446	434	423	413	402	391	380
10.0	370	359	349	338	328	318	308	297	287	277

S (x)

x	0	1	2	3	4	5	6	7	8	9
5.0	.4659	642	625	608	592	575	558	541	525	508
1	492	476	459	443	427	411	395	380	364	348
2	333	317	302	287	272	257	242	227	212	198
3	183	169	155	140	126	113	099	085	072	058
4	045	032	018	006	*993	*980	*967	*955	*943	*930
5	.3918	906	895	883	871	860	849	838	827	816
6	805	794	784	774	764	754	744	734	724	715
7	706	697	688	679	670	662	653	645	637	629
8	621	614	606	599	592	585	578	571	565	558
9	552	546	540	534	529	523	518	513	508	503
6.0	499	494	490	486	482	478	474	471	467	464
1	461	458	455	453	451	448	446	444	443	441
2	440	438	437	436	436	435	435	434	434	434
3	434	435	435	436	437	438	439	440	442	443
4	445	447	449	451	454	456	459	462	465	468
5	471	474	478	482	486	490	494	498	503	507
6	512	517	522	527	533	538	544	549	555	561
7	568	574	580	587	594	600	607	615	622	629
8	637	644	652	660	668	676	684	693	701	710
9	718	727	736	745	754	764	773	783	792	802
7.0	812	822	832	842	852	863	873	884	895	905
1	916	927	938	949	961	972	983	995	*006	*018
2	.4030	042	054	066	078	090	102	114	127	139
3	152	164	177	190	202	215	228	241	254	267
4	281	294	307	320	334	347	361	374	388	401
5	415	429	442	456	470	484	498	511	525	539
6	553	567	581	595	610	624	638	652	666	680
7	695	709	723	737	751	766	780	794	808	823
8	837	851	866	880	894	908	922	937	951	965
9	979	993	*008	*022	*036	*050	*064	*078	*092	*106
8.0	.5120	134	148	162	176	189	203	217	231	244
1	258	272	285	299	312	325	339	352	365	378
2	392	405	418	431	444	456	469	482	495	507
3	520	532	545	557	569	581	593	605	617	629
4	641	653	664	676	687	699	710	721	733	744
5	755	765	776	787	798	808	818	829	839	849
6	859	869	879	889	898	908	917	927	936	945
7	954	963	972	981	989	998	*006	*014	*022	*030
8	.6038	046	054	061	069	076	083	091	098	104
9	111	118	124	131	137	143	149	155	161	167
9.0	172	178	183	188	193	198	203	207	212	216
1	221	225	229	233	237	240	244	247	250	253
2	256	259	262	265	267	269	272	274	276	278
3	279	281	282	284	285	286	287	287	288	289
4	289	289	289	289	289	289	289	288	287	287
5	286	285	284	282	281	279	278	276	274	272
6	270	267	265	262	260	257	254	251	248	244
7	241	237	234	230	226	222	218	214	209	205
8	200	195	191	186	181	175	170	165	159	153
9	148	142	136	130	124	117	111	104	098	091
10.0	084	077	070	063	056	049	041	034	026	019

I

Ei (−x)

x	0	1	2	3	4	5	6	7	8	9
0.0	− ∞	4.038	3.355	2.959	2.681	2.468	2.295	2.151	2.027	1.919
1	−1.823	737	660	589	524	464	409	358	310	265
2	223	183	145	110	076	044	0139	*9849	*9573	*9309
3	−0.9057	8815	8583	8361	8147	7942	7745	7554	7371	7194
4	−0.7024	6859	6700	6546	6397	6253	6114	5979	5848	5721
5	−0.5598	5478	5362	5250	5140	5034	4930	4830	4732	4636
6	−0.4544	454	366	280	197	115	036	*959	*883	*810
7	−0.3738	668	599	532	467	403	341	280	221	163
8	106	050	*996	*943	*891	*840	*790	*742	*694	*647
9	−0.2602	557	513	470	429	387	347	308	269	231
1.0	194	157	122	087	052	019	*986	*953	*922	*890
1	−0.1860	830	801	772	743	716	688	662	635	609
2	584	559	535	511	487	464	441	419	397	376
3	355	334	313	293	274	254	235	216	198	180
4	162	145	128	111	094	078	062	046	030	015
5	0002	*9854	*9709	*9567	*9426	*9288	*9152	*9019	*8887	*8758
6	$-10^{-1} \times$ 0.8631	506	383	261	142	025	*909	*796	*684	*574
7	.7465	359	254	151	049	*949	*850	*753	*658	*564
8	.6471	380	290	202	115	029	*945	*862	*780	*700
9	.5620	542	465	390	315	241	169	098	027	*958
2.0	.4890	823	757	692	627	564	502	440	380	320
1	261	204	147	090	035	*980	*927	*874	*821	*770
2	.3719	669	620	571	523	476	430	384	339	294
3	250	207	164	122	081	040	000	*960	*921	*882
4	.2844	806	769	733	697	662	627	592	558	525
5	491	459	427	395	364	333	303	273	243	214
6	185	157	129	101	074	047	021	*994	*969	*943
7	.1918	893	869	845	821	798	775	752	730	707
8	686	664	643	622	601	581	560	540	521	502
9	482	464	445	427	409	391	373	356	338	322
3.0	305	288	272	256	240	225	209	194	179	164
1	149	135	121	107	093	079	066	052	039	026
2	013	0006	*9882	*9758	*9637	*9517	*9398	*9281	*9166	*9052
3	$-10^{-2} \times$ 0.8939	828	718	610	503	398	294	191	090	*990
4	.7891	793	697	602	508	416	324	234	145	057
5	.6970	884	800	716	634	552	472	393	314	237
6	160	085	011	*937	*864	*793	*722	*652	*583	*515
7	.5448	381	316	251	187	124	062	000	*939	*879
8	.4820	762	704	647	591	535	480	426	372	319
9	267	216	165	114	065	016	*967	*919	*872	*825
4.0	.3779	734	689	645	601	557	515	472	431	390
1	349	309	269	230	191	153	115	078	041	005
2	.2969	933	898	864	829	796	762	729	697	665
3	633	602	571	540	510	480	450	421	393	364
4	336	308	281	254	227	201	175	149	123	098
5	073	049	025	001	*977	*954	*931	*908	*885	*863
6	.1841	819	798	777	756	735	715	694	674	655
7	635	616	597	578	560	541	523	505	488	470
8	453	436	419	402	386	370	354	338	322	307
9	291	276	261	247	232	218	204	189	176	162
5.0	148	135	122	109	096	083	070	058	045	033

$\overline{\mathrm{Ei}}\ x$

x	0	1	2	3	4	5	6	7	8	9
0.0	− ∞	4.018	3.315	2.899	2.601	2.368	2.175	2.011	1.867	1.739
1	− 1.623	517	419	329	244	164	089	0172	*9491	*8841
2	− 0.8218	7619	7042	6485	5947	5425	4919	4427	3949	3482
3	− .3027	2582	2147	1721	1304	0894	0493	0098	*0290	*0672
4	+ .1048	1418	1783	2143	2498	2849	3195	3537	3876	4211
5	.4542	4870	5195	5517	5836	6153	6467	6778	7087	7394
6	.7699	8002	8302	8601	8898	9194	9488	9780	*0071	*036
7	1.065	094	122	151	179	207	236	264	292	320
8	347	375	403	431	458	486	513	541	568	595
9	623	650	677	705	732	759	786	814	841	868
1.0	895	922	949	977	*004	*031	*058	*086	*113	*140
1	2.167	195	222	249	277	304	332	359	387	414
2	442	470	498	525	553	581	609	637	665	693
3	721	750	778	806	835	863	892	921	949	978
4	3.007	036	065	094	124	153	183	212	242	271
5	301	331	361	391	422	452	482	513	544	574
6	605	636	667	699	730	762	793	825	857	889
7	921	953	986	*018	*051	*084	*117	*150	*183	*216
8	4.250	284	317	351	386	420	454	489	524	559
9	594	629	664	700	736	772	808	844	881	917
2.0	954	991	*028	*066	*104	*141	*179	*217	*256	*111
1	5.333	372	411	451	490	530	570	611	651	294
2	733	774	815	857	899	941	983	*025	*068	*692
3	6.154	198	242	286	330	374	419	464	509	555
4	601	647	693	740	787	834	881	929	977	*025
5	7.074	123	172	221	271	321	372	422	473	524
6	576	628	680	733	786	839	893	947	*001	*055
7	8.110	166	221	277	334	390	447	505	563	621
8	679	738	798	857	917	978	*039	*100	*162	*224
9	9.286	349	412	476	540	605	670	735	801	867
3.0	934	*001	*07	*14	*21	*27	*34	*41	*48	*55
1	10 × 1.063	070	077	084	092	099	106	114	122	129
2	137	144	152	160	168	176	184	192	200	208
3	216	224	233	241	249	258	266	275	284	292
4	301	310	319	328	337	346	355	364	374	383
5	393	402	412	421	431	441	451	460	470	480
6	491	501	511	521	532	542	553	564	574	585
7	596	607	618	629	640	652	663	675	686	698
8	709	721	733	745	757	769	782	794	806	819
9	832	844	857	870	883	896	909	923	936	949
4.0	963	977	991	*005	*019	*033	*047	*061	*076	*090
1	2.105	120	135	150	165	180	195	211	226	242
2	258	274	290	306	322	339	355	372	389	406
3	423	440	457	475	492	510	528	546	564	582
4	601	619	638	657	676	695	715	734	754	773
5	793	813	834	854	875	895	916	937	958	980
6	3.001	023	045	067	089	112	134	157	180	203
7	226	250	274	297	321	346	370	395	420	445
8	470	495	521	547	573	599	625	652	679	706
9	733	761	788	816	845	873	902	931	960	989
5.0	4.019	048	078	109	139	170	201	232	264	296

I*

MISCELLANEOUS TRANSCENDENTAL FUNCTIONS

Ei (−x)

x	0	1	2	3	4	5	6	7	8	9
5.0	−10⁻²× 0.1148	135	122	109	096	083	070	058	045	033
1	021	0094	*9977	*9861	*9746	*9633	*9521	*9410	*9301	*9193
2	−10⁻³× 0.9086	8981	8877	8774	8672	8571	8472	8374	8277	8181
3	.8086	7992	7900	7809	7718	7629	7541	7453	7367	7282
4	.7198	7115	7033	6952	6871	6792	6714	6636	6560	6484
5	.6409	335	262	190	119	048	*979	*910	*842	*775
6	.5708	643	578	514	450	388	326	265	204	145
7	085	027	*969	*912	*856	*800	*745	*691	*637	*584
8	.4532	480	428	378	328	278	229	181	133	086
9	039	*993	*947	*902	*858	*814	*770	*727	*684	*642
6.0	.3601	560	519	479	439	400	361	323	285	248
1	211	174	138	102	067	032	*998	*964	*930	*897
2	.2864	831	799	767	736	705	674	644	614	584
3	555	526	497	469	441	413	386	359	332	306
4	279	254	228	203	178	153	129	105	081	058
5	034	011	*989	*966	*944	*922	*900	*879	*858	*837
6	.1816	795	775	755	735	716	696	677	658	640
7	621	603	585	567	549	532	515	498	481	464
8	448	431	415	399	384	368	353	337	322	308
9	293	278	264	250	236	222	208	195	181	168
7.0	155	142	129	116	104	092	079	067	055	043
1	032	020	0087	*9974	*9863	*9752	*9643	*9535	*9429	*9323
2	−10⁻⁴× .09219	9116	9014	8913	8813	8715	8617	8521	8426	8332
3	.8239	8147	8056	7966	7877	7789	7702	7616	7531	7447
4	.7364	7282	7201	7120	7041	6962	6885	6808	6732	6657
5	.6583	510	437	366	295	225	155	087	019	*952
6	.5886	820	756	692	628	566	504	443	382	322
7	263	205	147	090	033	*977	*922	*867	*813	*760
8	.4707	655	603	552	502	452	402	354	305	258
9	210	164	118	072	027	*982	*938	*895	*851	*809
8.0	.3767	725	684	643	603	563	523	484	446	408
1	370	333	296	259	223	188	153	118	083	049
2	015	*982	*949	*917	*884	*853	*821	*790	*759	*729
3	.2699	669	639	610	582	553	525	497	470	442
4	415	389	362	336	311	285	260	235	211	186
5	162	138	115	091	068	046	023	001	*979	*957
6	.1936	914	893	872	852	832	811	791	772	752
7	733	714	695	677	658	640	622	604	587	569
8	552	535	518	501	485	469	452	437	421	405
9	390	375	359	345	330	315	301	287	272	259
9.0	245	231	218	204	191	178	165	152	140	127
1	115	103	091	079	067	055	044	032	021	0099
2	−10⁻⁵× 0.9988	879	771	664	558	454	351	248	147	047
3	.8948	851	754	658	564	470	378	286	196	106
4	018	*930	*844	*758	*674	*590	*507	*425	*344	*264
5	.7185	106	029	*952	*876	*802	*727	*654	*582	*510
6	.6439	369	299	231	163	096	029	*964	*899	*834
7	.5771	708	646	584	524	464	404	345	287	230
8	173	116	061	006	*951	*897	*844	*791	*739	*688
9	.4637	586	537	487	439	390	343	295	249	203
10.0	157	112	067	023	*979	*936	*893	*851	*809	*768

Ēi x

x	0	1	2	3	4	5	6	7	8	9
5.0	10 × 4.019	048	078	109	139	170	201	232	264	296
1	328	360	392	425	458	492	525	559	593	628
2	662	697	733	768	804	840	877	914	951	988
3	5.026	064	102	140	179	218	258	298	338	379
4	419	461	502	544	586	629	671	715	758	802
5	847	891	936	982	*027	*074	*120	*167	*214	*262
6	6.310	359	408	457	507	557	607	658	709	761
7	813	866	919	973	*027	*081	*136	*191	*247	*303
8	7.360	417	475	533	592	651	710	770	831	892
9	954	*016	*079	*142	*205	*270	*334	*400	*466	*532
6.0	8.599	666	735	803	872	942	*013	*084	*155	*227
1	9.300	374	448	522	598	673	750	827	905	983
2	10²× 1.0063	014	022	030	039	047	055	064	072	081
3	089	098	107	115	124	133	142	151	161	170
4	179	189	198	208	218	227	237	247	257	267
5	277	288	298	309	319	330	340	351	362	373
6	384	395	407	418	430	441	453	465	476	488
7	501	513	525	537	550	562	575	588	601	614
8	627	640	654	667	681	695	708	722	736	751
9	765	779	794	809	823	838	853	869	884	899
7.0	915	931	947	963	979	995	*012	*028	*045	*062
1	2.079	096	113	131	148	166	184	202	220	238
2	257	276	294	313	333	352	371	391	411	431
3	451	472	492	513	534	555	576	597	619	641
4	663	685	708	730	753	776	799	822	846	870
5	894	918	943	967	992	*017	*042	*068	*094	*120
6	3.146	172	199	226	253	280	308	335	364	392
7	420	449	478	508	537	567	597	627	658	689
8	720	751	783	815	847	880	913	946	979	*013
9	4.047	081	116	151	186	222	257	293	330	367
8.0	404	441	479	517	555	594	633	673	713	753
1	793	834	875	917	959	*001	*044	*087	*130	*174
2	5.218	263	308	353	399	445	492	539	586	634
3	682	731	780	830	880	930	981	*032	*084	*136
4	6.189	242	296	350	405	460	515	571	628	685
5	743	801	859	918	978	*038	*099	*160	*222	*284
6	7.347	411	475	539	604	670	736	803	871	939
7	8.007	077	147	217	288	360	433	506	579	654
8	729	805	881	958	*036	*114	*194	*273	*354	*435
9	9.517	600	684	768	853	938	*025	*11	*20	*29
9.0	10³× 1.038	047	056	065	075	084	093	103	113	122
1	132	142	152	162	172	182	193	203	214	224
2	235	246	257	268	279	290	301	313	324	336
3	347	359	371	383	395	408	420	432	445	458
4	471	483	496	510	523	536	550	563	577	591
5	605	619	633	648	662	677	692	707	722	737
6	752	768	783	799	815	831	847	863	880	896
7	913	930	947	964	982	999	*017	*035	*053	*071
8	2.089	108	126	145	164	183	202	222	242	262
9	282	302	322	343	364	385	406	427	449	470
10.0	492	514	537	559	582	605	628	651	675	699

MISCELLANEOUS TRANSCENDENTAL FUNCTIONS

Ci x

x	0	1	2	3	4	5	6	7	8	9
0.0	− ∞	4.028	3.335	2.930	2.642	2.419	2.237	2.083	1.950	1.833
1	− 1.728	633	547	467	394	326	262	202	146	093
2	0422	*9944	*9490	*9057	*8643	*8247	*7867	*7503	*7153	*6816
3	− 0.6492	6179	5877	5585	5304	5031	4767	4511	4263	4022
4	− .3788	3561	3341	3126	2918	2715	2517	2325	2138	1956
5	− .1778	1605	1436	1271	1110	0953	0800	0650	0504	0362
6	− .0223	0087	*0046	*0176	*0303	*0426	*0548	*0666	*0782	*0895
7	+ .1005	113	219	322	423	522	618	712	805	895
8	983	*069	*153	*235	*316	*394	*471	*546	*619	*691
9	+ .2761	829	896	961	*024	*086	*147	*206	*263	*319
1.0	+ .3374	427	479	530	579	627	674	720	764	807
1	849	889	929	967	*004	*040	*075	*109	*142	*174
2	+ .4205	234	263	291	317	343	368	392	414	436
3	457	478	497	515	533	549	565	580	594	608
4	620	632	643	653	662	671	679	686	693	698
5	704	708	712	715	717	719	720	720	720	719
6	717	715	712	709	705	701	696	690	684	677
7	670	662	653	645	635	625	615	604	592	580
8	568	555	542	528	514	499	484	469	453	436
9	419	402	385	367	348	329	310	291	271	250
2.0	230	209	187	166	144	122	099	076	053	029
1	005	*981	*956	*932	*907	*881	*856	*830	*804	*777
2	+ .3751	724	697	669	642	614	586	558	529	501
3	472	443	413	384	354	325	295	264	234	204
4	173	142	111	080	049	017	*986	*954	*923	*891
5	+ .2859	827	794	762	730	697	665	632	599	566
6	533	500	467	434	401	368	334	301	268	234
7	201	167	134	100	067	033	*999	*966	*932	*899
8	+ .1865	831	798	764	730	697	663	630	596	562
9	529	495	462	429	395	362	329	296	262	229
3.0	196	163	130	098	065	032	*9995	*9670	*9346	*9022
1	+10⁻¹× 0.8699	8377	8056	7736	7417	7100	6783	6467	6152	5838
2	.5526	5214	4904	4595	4287	3981	3676	3372	3069	2768
3	.2468	2169	1872	1576	1282	0989	0698	0408	0120	*0167
4	−10⁻¹× 0.0452	0735	1017	1298	1576	1853	2129	2402	2674	2944
5	.3213	3480	3744	4008	4269	4528	4786	5042	5295	5547
6	.5797	6046	6292	6536	6778	7019	7257	7493	7728	7960
7	.8190	8418	8644	8868	9090	9310	9528	9744	9957	*0169
8	−10⁰ × 0.1038	058	079	099	119	139	159	178	197	216
9	235	253	272	290	308	325	343	360	377	393
4.0	410	426	442	458	473	489	504	519	533	548
1	562	576	589	603	616	629	642	654	666	678
2	690	702	713	724	735	746	756	766	776	786
3	795	804	813	822	831	839	847	855	862	870
4	877	883	890	897	903	909	914	920	925	930
5	935	939	944	948	952	955	959	962	965	968
6	970	973	975	977	978	980	981	982	983	984
7	984	984	984	984	983	983	982	981	979	978
8	976	974	972	970	967	964	961	958	955	952
9	948	944	940	936	931	926	922	916	911	906
5.0	900	895	889	882	876	870	863	856	849	842

Si x

x	0	1	2	3	4	5	6	7	8	9
0.0	.0000	100	200	300	400	500	600	700	800	900
1	.0999	*099	*199	*299	*398	*498	*598	*697	*797	*896
2	.1996	*095	*194	*293	*392	*491	*590	*689	*788	*886
3	.2985	*083	*182	*280	*378	*476	*574	*672	*770	*867
4	.3965	*062	*159	*256	*353	*450	*546	*643	*739	*835
5	.4931	*027	*123	*218	*313	*408	*503	*598	*693	*787
6	.5881	975	*069	*163	*256	*349	*442	*535	*628	*720
7	.6812	904	996	*087	*179	*270	*360	*451	*541	*631
8	.7721	811	900	989	*078	*166	*254	*342	*430	*518
9	.8605	692	778	865	951	*036	*122	*207	*292	*377
1.0	.9461	545	629	712	795	878	960	*042	*12	*21
1	1.029	037	045	053	061	069	077	085	092	100
2	108	116	124	131	139	146	154	162	169	177
3	184	191	199	206	213	221	228	235	242	249
4	256	263	270	277	284	291	298	305	311	318
5	325	331	338	344	351	357	364	370	377	383
6	389	395	402	408	414	420	426	432	438	444
7	450	455	461	467	473	478	484	489	495	500
8	506	511	517	522	527	532	538	543	548	553
9	558	563	568	573	577	582	587	592	596	601
2.0	1.605	10	14	19	23	28	32	36	40	45
1	49	53	57	61	65	69	73	76	80	84
2	88	91	95	98	*02	*05	*09	*12	*16	*19
3	1.722	25	29	32	35	38	41	44	47	50
4	52	55	58	61	63	66	69	71	74	76
5	79	81	83	86	88	90	92	94	96	98
6	1.800	02	04	06	08	10	12	13	15	17
7	18	20	21	23	24	26	27	28	30	31
8	32	33	34	36	37	38	39	40	40	41
9	42	43	44	45	45	46	46	47	48	48
3.0	49	49	50	50	50	51	51	51	51	52
1	52	52	52	52	52	52	52	52	52	52
2	51	51	51	51	50	50	50	49	49	49
3	48	48	47	47	46	45	45	44	43	43
4	42	41	40	40	39	38	37	36	35	34
5	33	32	31	30	29	28	27	26	24	23
6	22	21	19	18	17	16	14	13	11	10
7	09	07	06	04	03	01	00	*98	*97	*95
8	1.793	92	90	88	87	85	83	82	80	78
9	77	75	73	71	69	68	66	64	62	60
4.0	58	56	54	52	51	49	47	45	43	41
1	39	37	35	33	31	29	27	25	23	20
2	18	16	14	12	10	08	06	04	02	*99
3	1.697	95	93	91	89	87	84	82	80	78
4	76	74	72	69	67	65	63	61	58	56
5	54	52	50	48	45	43	41	39	37	35
6	32	30	28	26	24	22	20	17	15	13
7	11	09	07	05	03	00	*98	*96	*94	*92
8	1.590	88	86	84	82	80	78	76	74	72
9	70	68	66	64	62	60	58	56	54	52
5.0	50	48	46	44	42	40	39	37	35	33

Ci x

x	0	1	2	3	4	5	6	7	8	9
5.0	− 0.1900	895	889	882	876	870	863	856	849	842
1	835	827	820	812	804	796	787	779	770	761
2	753	743	734	725	715	706	696	686	676	665
3	655	645	634	623	612	601	590	579	567	556
4	544	532	520	508	496	484	471	459	446	433
5	421	408	395	381	368	355	341	328	314	301
6	287	273	259	245	231	216	202	188	173	159
7	144	129	115	100	085	070	055	040	025	010
8	$-10^{-1} \times$ 0.9944	9791	9638	9484	9329	9174	9019	8863	8707	8550
9	.8393	8236	8078	7920	7762	7603	7444	7285	7125	6966
6.0	.6806	6646	6485	6325	6164	6003	5843	5682	5521	5359
1	.5198	5037	4876	4715	4553	4392	4231	4070	3909	3748
2	.3587	3427	3266	3106	2946	2786	2626	2466	2307	2148
3	.1989	1830	1672	1514	1356	1199	1042	0886	0729	0574
4	.0418	0263	0109	*0045	*0199	*0352	*0505	*0657	*0809	*0960
5	$+10^{-1} \times$ 0.1110	1260	1409	1558	1706	1854	2001	2147	2293	2438
6	.2582	2726	2869	3011	3153	3293	3433	3573	3711	3849
7	.3986	4122	4257	4391	4525	4658	4789	4920	5051	5180
8	.5308	5435	5562	5687	5812	5936	6058	6180	6301	6421
9	.6539	6657	6774	6889	7004	7118	7230	7342	7452	7561
7.0	.7670	7777	7883	7988	8092	8194	8296	8396	8496	8594
1	.8691	8787	8881	8975	9067	9158	9248	9337	9424	9511
2	.9596	9680	9762	9844	9924	*0002	*008	*016	*023	*031
3	$+10^{0} \times$ 0.1038	045	052	059	066	072	079	085	091	098
4	104	109	115	121	126	132	137	142	147	152
5	156	161	165	170	174	178	182	185	189	193
6	196	199	202	205	208	211	213	216	218	220
7	222	224	226	228	229	231	232	233	234	235
8	236	236	237	237	238	238	238	238	237	237
9	236	236	235	234	233	232	231	229	228	226
8.0	224	222	220	218	216	214	211	209	206	203
1	200	197	194	191	187	184	180	176	172	168
2	164	160	156	152	147	142	138	133	128	123
3	118	112	107	102	096	090	085	079	073	067
4	061	054	048	042	035	029	022	015	008	0014
5	$+10^{-1} \times$ 0.9943	9872	9800	9727	9653	9579	9503	9427	9350	9272
6	.9194	9114	9034	8953	8872	8790	8707	8623	8539	8454
7	.8368	8282	8195	8107	8019	7930	7840	7750	7659	7568
8	.7476	7384	7291	7197	7103	7008	6913	6818	6722	6625
9	.6528	6431	6333	6234	6136	6036	5937	5837	5737	5636
9.0	.5535	5433	5332	5230	5127	5024	4922	4818	4715	4611
1	.4507	4403	4298	4193	4089	3983	3878	3773	3667	3561
2	.3455	3349	3243	3137	3031	2924	2818	2711	2605	2498
3	.2391	2285	2178	2071	1965	1858	1751	1645	1538	1432
4	.1325	1219	1113	1007	0901	0795	0689	0584	0478	0373
5	.0268	0163	0058	*0046	*0150	*0254	*0358	*0462	*0565	*0668
6	$-10^{-1} \times$ 0.0771	0873	0975	1077	1179	1280	1381	1481	1581	1681
7	.1780	1879	1978	2076	2174	2272	2368	2465	2561	2657
8	.2752	2847	2941	3035	3128	3221	3313	3404	3496	3586
9	.3676	3766	3855	3943	4031	4118	4205	4291	4377	4461
10.0	.4546	4629	4712	4794	4876	4957	5038	5117	5196	5275

Si x

x	0	1	2	3	4	5	6	7	8	9
5.0	1.550	48	46	44	42	40	39	37	35	33
1	31	29	28	26	24	22	21	19	17	15
2	14	12	10	09	07	05	04	02	00	*99
3	1.497	96	94	93	91	90	88	87	85	84
4	82	81	79	78	77	75	74	73	71	70
5	69	67	66	65	64	63	61	60	59	58
6	57	56	54	53	52	51	50	49	48	47
7	46	45	44	43	42	42	41	40	39	38
8	37	37	36	35	34	34	33	32	31	31
9	30	30	29	28	28	27	27	26	26	25
6.0	25	24	24	23	23	23	22	22	21	21
1	21	21	20	20	20	20	19	19	19	19
2	19	19	18	18	18	18	18	18	18	18
3	18	18	18	18	18	19	19	19	19	19
4	19	19	20	20	20	20	21	21	21	21
5	22	22	22	23	23	24	24	24	25	25
6	26	26	27	27	28	28	29	29	30	31
7	31	32	32	33	34	34	35	36	36	37
8	38	39	39	40	41	42	42	43	44	45
9	46	47	47	48	49	50	51	52	53	54
7.0	55	56	56	57	58	59	60	61	62	63
1	64	65	67	68	69	70	71	72	73	74
2	75	76	77	78	80	81	82	83	84	85
3	86	88	89	90	91	92	94	95	96	97
4	98	*00	*01	*02	*03	*04	*06	*07	*08	*09
5	1.511	12	13	14	16	17	18	20	21	22
6	23	25	26	27	28	30	31	32	34	35
7	36	37	39	40	41	43	44	45	46	48
8	49	50	51	53	54	55	57	58	59	60
9	62	63	64	65	67	68	69	70	72	73
8.0	74	75	77	78	79	80	82	83	84	85
1	86	88	89	90	91	92	93	95	96	97
2	98	99	*00	*02	*03	*04	*05	*06	*07	*08
3	1.609	10	11	13	14	15	16	17	18	19
4	20	21	22	23	24	25	26	27	28	29
5	30	31	31	32	33	34	35	36	37	38
6	39	39	40	41	42	43	44	44	45	46
7	47	47	48	49	50	50	51	52	52	53
8	54	54	55	56	56	57	58	58	59	59
9	60	60	61	62	62	63	63	64	64	65
9.0	65	65	66	66	67	67	68	68	68	69
1	69	69	70	70	70	71	71	71	72	72
2	72	72	73	73	73	73	73	73	74	74
3	74	74	74	74	74	74	75	75	75	75
4	75	75	75	75	75	75	75	75	75	75
5	74	74	74	74	74	74	74	74	73	73
6	73	73	73	73	72	72	72	72	71	71
7	71	71	70	70	70	69	69	69	68	68
8	68	67	67	66	66	66	65	65	64	64
9	63	63	62	62	61	61	60	60	59	59
10.0	58	58	57	57	56	56	55	54	54	53

MISCELLANEOUS TRANSCENDENTAL FUNCTIONS

$$\Gamma(x) = y!$$

x	y	0	1	2	3	4	5	6	7	8	9
1.00	0.00	1.0000	*94	*88	*83	*77	*71	*66	*60	*54	*49
1	1	0.9943	38	32	27	21	16	10	05	*99	*94
2	2	.9888	83	78	72	67	62	56	51	46	41
3	3	35	30	25	20	15	10	05	00	*94	*89
4	4	.9784	79	74	69	64	59	55	50	45	40
5	5	35	30	25	21	16	11	06	02	*97	*92
6	6	.9687	83	78	73	69	64	60	55	51	46
7	7	42	37	33	28	24	19	15	10	06	02
8	8	.9597	93	89	84	80	76	71	67	63	59
9	9	55	50	46	42	38	34	30	26	22	18
1.10	.10	14	09	05	01	*98	*94	*90	*86	*82	*78
1	1	.9474	70	66	62	59	55	51	47	43	40
2	2	36	32	28	25	21	17	14	10	07	03
3	3	.9399	96	92	89	85	82	78	75	71	68
4	4	64	61	57	54	50	47	44	40	37	34
5	5	30	27	24	21	17	14	11	08	04	01
6	6	.9298	95	92	89	85	82	79	76	73	70
7	7	67	64	61	58	55	52	49	46	43	40
8	8	37	34	31	29	26	23	20	17	14	12
9	9	09	06	03	01	*98	*95	*92	*90	*87	*84
1.20	.20	.9182	79	76	74	71	69	66	63	61	58
1	1	56	53	51	48	46	43	41	38	36	33
2	2	31	29	26	24	22	19	17	14	12	10
3	3	08	05	03	01	*98	*96	*94	*92	*90	*87
4	4	.9085	83	81	79	77	74	72	70	68	66
5	5	64	62	60	58	56	54	52	50	48	46
6	6	44	42	40	38	36	34	32	31	29	27
7	7	25	23	21	20	18	16	14	12	11	09
8	8	07	05	04	02	00	*99	*97	*95	*94	*92
9	9	.8990	89	87	86	84	82	81	79	78	76
1.30	.30	75	73	72	70	69	67	66	64	63	61
1	1	60	59	57	56	54	53	52	50	49	48
2	2	46	45	44	43	41	40	39	37	36	35
3	3	34	33	31	30	29	28	27	26	24	23
4	4	22	21	20	19	18	17	16	15	14	13
5	5	12	11	10	09	08	07	06	05	04	03
6	6	02	01	00	*99	*98	*97	*97	*96	*95	*94
7	7	.8893	92	92	91	90	89	88	88	87	86
8	8	85	85	84	83	83	82	81	80	80	79
9	9	79	78	77	77	76	75	75	74	74	73
1.40	.40	73	72	72	71	71	70	70	69	69	68
1	1	68	67	67	66	66	65	65	65	64	64
2	2	64	63	63	63	62	62	62	61	61	61
3	3	60	60	60	60	59	59	59	59	58	58
4	4	58	58	58	58	57	57	57	57	57	57
5	5	57	57	56	56	56	56	56	56	56	56
6	6	56	56	56	56	56	56	56	56	56	56
7	7	56	56	56	57	57	57	57	57	57	57
8	8	57	58	58	58	58	58	59	59	59	59
9	9	59	60	60	60	60	61	61	61	62	62
1.50	0.50	62	63	63	63	64	64	64	65	65	66

$\Gamma(x) = y!$

x	y	0	1	2	3	4	5	6	7	8	9
1.50	0.50	0.8862	63	63	63	64	64	64	65	65	66
I	I	66	66	67	67	68	68	69	69	69	70
2	2	70	71	71	72	72	73	73	74	75	75
3	3	76	76	77	77	78	79	79	80	80	81
4	4	82	82	83	84	84	85	86	87	87	88
5	5	89	89	90	91	92	92	93	94	95	96
6	6	96	97	98	99	*00	*01	*01	*02	*03	*04
7	7	.8905	06	07	08	09	09	10	11	12	13
8	8	14	15	16	17	18	19	20	21	22	23
9	9	24	25	26	27	29	30	31	32	33	34
1.60	.60	35	36	37	39	40	41	42	43	44	46
I	I	47	48	49	50	52	53	54	55	57	58
2	2	59	61	62	63	64	66	67	68	70	71
3	3	72	74	75	77	78	79	81	82	84	85
4	4	86	88	89	91	92	94	95	97	98	*00
5	5	.9001	03	04	06	07	09	10	12	14	15
6	6	17	18	20	21	23	25	26	28	30	31
7	7	33	35	36	38	40	41	43	45	47	48
8	8	50	52	54	55	57	59	61	62	64	66
9	9	68	70	71	73	75	77	79	81	83	84
1.70	.70	86	88	90	92	94	96	98	*00	*02	*04
I	I	.9106	08	10	12	14	16	18	20	22	24
2	2	26	28	30	32	34	36	38	40	42	45
3	3	47	49	51	53	55	57	60	62	64	66
4	4	68	70	73	75	77	79	82	84	86	88
5	5	91	93	95	97	*00	*02	*04	*07	*09	*11
6	6	.9214	16	18	21	23	26	28	30	33	35
7	7	38	40	42	45	47	50	52	55	57	60
8	8	62	65	67	70	72	75	77	80	83	85
9	9	88	90	93	95	98	*01	*03	*06	*09	*11
1.80	.80	.9314	16	19	22	25	27	30	33	35	38
I	I	41	43	46	49	52	55	57	60	63	66
2	2	68	71	74	77	80	83	85	88	91	94
3	3	97	*00	*03	*06	*08	*11	*14	*17	*20	*23
4	4	.9426	29	32	35	38	41	44	47	50	53
5	5	56	59	62	65	68	71	74	78	81	84
6	6	87	90	93	96	99	*03	*06	*09	*12	*15
7	7	.9518	22	25	28	31	34	38	41	44	47
8	8	51	54	57	61	64	67	70	74	77	80
9	9	84	87	91	94	97	*01	*04	*07	*11	*14
1.90	.90	.9618	21	25	28	31	35	38	42	45	49
I	I	52	56	59	63	66	70	73	77	81	84
2	2	88	91	95	99	*02	*06	*09	*13	*17	*20
3	3	.9724	28	31	35	39	42	46	50	54	57
4	4	61	65	68	72	76	80	84	87	91	95
5	5	99	*03	*06	*10	*14	*18	*22	*26	*30	*34
6	6	.9837	41	45	49	53	57	61	65	69	73
7	7	77	81	85	89	93	97	*01	*05	*09	*13
8	8	.9917	21	25	29	33	38	42	46	50	54
9	9	58	62	66	71	75	79	83	87	92	96
2.00	1.00	1.0000	04	08	13	17	21	26	30	34	38

V. TRANSCENDENTAL CONSTANTS

1. *Definitions*

$$\pi = 4 \left(1 - \tfrac{1}{3} + \frac{1}{5} - \frac{1}{7} + - \ldots \right)$$

$$e = \lim_{n \to \infty} \left(1 + \frac{1}{n} \right)^n = 1 + \frac{1}{1!} + \frac{1}{2!} + \frac{1}{3!} + \ldots$$

$$\ln \gamma = \lim \left(1 + \tfrac{1}{2} + \tfrac{1}{3} + \tfrac{1}{4} + \ldots + \frac{1}{n} - \ln n \right)$$

2. *Numerical values*

$\pi = 3.142$	$1/\pi = 0.3183$
$\pi^2 = 9.870$	$\sqrt{\pi} = 1.772$
$\pi^3 = 31.01$	
$e = 2.718$	$1/e = 0.3679$
$\log e = 0.4343$	
$\ln 10 = 2.303$	
$\gamma = 1.781$	$\gamma/2 = 0.8905$
$\ln \gamma = 0.5772$	$\ln \dfrac{\gamma}{2} = -0.1159$
$1^\circ = 0.01745$	$1 = 57.30^\circ$